Russian
Legends

Russian Legends

Text by
Pola Weiss

Translated by
Alice Sachs

Crescent Books
New York

The legends

Where love is, God is
Let the fire burn, you cannot put it out
The three old men.

are by Leo Tolstoy

The legends

Story of Pierre, Prince of Murom, and his wife Fevronia
The young girl and the moon
The miraculous flower
Legend of the old bell-ringer
The two blind men
Martha and Mary
Legend of the Russian priest and his Polish enemy.

were adapted by
Lucienne Romé-Henchoz

First English edition published by
Editions Minerva S.A., Genève.
© MCMLXXX by Editions Minerva S.A., Genève.
All rights reserved.

Library of Congress Catalog Card
Number: 79-57029
ISBN: O-517-309246

This edition is published by Crescent Books,
a division of Crown Publishers, Inc.

a b c d e f g h

Printed in Italy

Contents

Fomushka
the village idiot

One evening toward the end of September, a group of young girls, young boys and children, gathered at the entrance to a large Russian village, were noisily laughing and singing. The sun was setting behind the mountain that bordered the village and could be climbed by a twisting path covered with black mud. The air was damp and cold; with the setting of the sun, the bands of light cutting across the gray sky had disappeared. In the village could be heard the creaking of some doors being closed and the threats and exhortations of a peasant helping his horse to free his wagon, that was stuck in the mud. A cow, that had stopped in the street and was stretching its neck, mooed at length, then went on to its familiar yard. A small boy in a short shirt without a belt, his bare feet sunk deep into the mud, imitated the cow, crying and sobbing so he could be heard throughout the village.

At that moment there appeared in the street a man in a black coverall, patched here and there with scraps of white, *laptis* on his feet, and on his head a huge torn cap from which hung the remnant of a torn visor. Underneath his ragged and revealing coverall could be seen a shirt of some coarse material, very dirty and very worn. A fragment of a broken fastener was still visible by a buttonhole of the collar. The shirt was not closed and provided the chest of the unhappy peasant with no protection against the damp chill of the autumn evening. In his hand was a long stick. His thin face, wan with a bluish pallor, his clouded eyes, his slow, unsteady gait, everything about him indicated an unhealthy condition and aroused pity for him even while it made a painful impression. His gaze had a childish quality quite inappropriate in a man of his age. He advanced slowly, sometimes looking to the side, sometimes bowing his head, sometimes frowning, sometimes looking quite merry. On his lips was an expression which was a cross between a smile and a grimace. This bizarre individual was commonly known as *Fomushka the village idiot.*

It is possible that at some time you may have seen poor Fomushka, when your horse and carriage, crossing our steppes and our endless plains, stopped in our village for a few minutes; amidst the disputatious *yamshchiki*, women offering their trifling wares, and the crowd who gaped at you, possibly you noticed *Fomushka the village idiot.* In that case, you undoubtedly observed how fearfully he looked at you, how he greeted you silently, how timidly he approached the door of your conveyance, with what fright he drew back when your footman called to him to get out of the way. Perhaps the strange creature captured the attention of the distracted traveler for a brief instant and you were about to throw him a few coins when your carriage started abruptly and in the twinkling of an eye you left far behind you the village and the crowd, and yielded yourself to dreams and sleeps, as if you had never perceived the face of poor Fomushka.

Born delicate, Fomushka was sickly for a long time, and was late and slow in developing. At an age when children usually walk and play, he could barely crawl. For many months his mother had to extend the period of infancy and carry him in her arms; she developed an aversion to him and was the first to call him an idiot, a name that would cling to him throughout his life. "He is already four years old," she said, "and neither walks nor speaks; I have to take care of him in addition to my other work." His father, who had to listen to her complaints, grew to dislike the child. The boy grew up without receiving any affection from the family, and continued to be described as an idiot.

The idiot was gentle, shy, and taciturn; his sisters teased him and his brothers tormented him, as did unrelated children, and the poor wretch could not count on being defended by either his father or his mother. Rebuffed by the children his own age, the idiot avoided their company and hid from them. Thus he grew up a loner, with no companion but himself. No one loved him except Kudlashka, the farmyard dog who guarded the house. At night, while he lay on the stove of the cabin, Fomushka the idiot derived great joy from the sound of his friend Kudlashka barking and, as soon as it was light, ran to join him, lay down beside him and, with him, warmed himself in the sun. In the summer, when his mother gave him a piece of dry bread and sent him to the fields to take care of the sow and her piglets through the livelong day, Kudlashka always accompanied him. Together, they spent the day in the meadow, in the midst of flowers and bushes, and together ate the piece of bread. When evening came and darkness fell, Fomushka reluctantly left the field and, assisted by Kudlashka, brought the pigs back to the house.

One summer day, as Fomushka made ready, as was his custom, to escort the sow to the lea, accompanied by Kudlashka, he observed that the latter seemed distressed; he frequently howled piteously and rested his muzzle on the knees of his friend. That evening, Kudlashka was still able to drag himself to the house, but Fomushka did not hear his voice at all that night. In the morning he found him under the lean-to; Kudlashka was already experiencing his death throes, but at the sight of his friend he made one last effort, wagged his tail and lifted his head. Fomushka sat down beside him, petted him and put his hand on the dog's back. Kudlashka yelped tenderly, stretched out and died. Fomushka uttered a loud cry such as had never before come out of his mouth and ran to the house. His mother, frightened, rushed to meet him. The child, pale as death, could only cry out: "Kudlashka! Kudlashka!" "Be quiet, imbecile," his mother commanded, gesturing threateningly with her fist. "What about Kudlashka?" The idiot stopped yelling; sobbing

11

Флеровъ

Печ. въ лит. П. Лухменева Изд. Покровскаго Москва 185_ год

МУЖИЧЕКЪ.

...Ъ ПОТРАВЪ,
...АРОМЪ ПОКАТИСЬ;
...ЕТЕЙ ДОМОВОЙ.
...ТЛОЮ ПОДМЕЛЪ;
...ДОКЪ ЗАДАМИ,
...ЯМЪ РАЗВЕЛЪ;
...ЛАВКОЙ СУНДУКЪ,
...НУТЬ ЛЕЖИТЪ
...ВШИСЬ ИЗБА,
...ТАРУШКА СТОИТЪ;

ВСПОМНИ ВРЕМЯ СВОЕ,
КАКЪ КАТИЛОСЬ ОНО;
ПО ПОЛЯМЪ, ПО ЛУГАМЪ,
ЗОЛОТОЙ РѢКОЙ;
СО ДВОРА И ГУМНА,
ПОДОРОЖКѢ БОЛЬШОЙ
ПО СЕЛАМЪ ГОРОДАМЪ,
ПО ТОРГОВЫМЪ ЛЮДЯМЪ;
И КАКЪ ДВЕРИ ЕМУ;

РАЗТВОРЯЛИ ВЕЗДѢ
И ВЪ ПОЧЕТНОМЪ ДОМУ,
БЫЛО МѢСТО ТВОЕ,
А ТЕПЕРЬ ПОДЪ ОКНОМЪ,
ТЫ СЪ БѢДОЮ СИДИШЬ,
И ВЕСЬ ДЕНЬ НА ПЕЧИ,
БЕЗЪ ПРОСЫПУ СПИШЬ,
И ВЪ ПОЛЯХЪ СИРОТОЙ,
ХЛѢБЪ НЕЖАТОЙ СТОИТЪ

ВѢТЕРЪ МЕЧЕТЪ ЗЕРНО,
ПТИЦА КЛЮЕТЪ ЕГО;
ЧТО ТЫ СПИШЬ МУЖИЧОКЪ
ВѢДЬ УЖЪ ЛѢТО ПРОШЛО
ВѢДЬ ОСЕНЬ УЖЪ НА ДВОРѢ
ЧРЕЗЪ ПРЯСЛО ГЛЯДИТЪ;
ВСЛѢДЪ ЗА НЕЮ ЗИМА,

ВЪ ТЕПЛОЙ ШУБѢ ИДЕТ
ПУТЬ СНѢЖКОМЪ ПОРОШ...
ПОДЪ САНЯМИ ХРУСТИТ
ВСѢ СОСѢДИ НА САНЯХ
ХЛѢБЪ ВЕЗУТЪ ПРОДА...
СОБИРАЮТ КАЗНУ...
ПИВО КОВШИЧКОМЪ П...

Изочин. Н. Покровскаго.

and trembling like a leaf, he had barely strength enough to say: "He is dead!" "Take him to the field," his mother ordered. The child took the dog on his arms and carried him to the field. After remaining seated for a long time near the corpse and weeping bitterly, he dug a hole there and put Kudlashka in it. Then he walked slowly back to the house, his head bent, and thereafter was alone and solitary when he led the sow to the grazing ground.

From that time on, Fomushka became still more taciturn, more listless, more unsociable. Although he grew big, he remained gentle, obedient, and passive; even when he was scolded or insulted, he did not react, but merely grew pale and lowered his eyes. He did exactly as he was ordered, plowed, sowed, mowed, threshed the wheat, and never refused to perform any chore requested of him. But nevertheless he acted curiously: if no particular task was assigned him, he remained completely idle; but if he was given a chore to do, he immediately went to work and continued without interruption, however tired he might be, until he had finished or was told to stop. If he was invited, he ate his meals with the family; otherwise he went without eating, enduring hunger and demanding nothing. When he returned from work in the evening, he lay down on the stove or in the closet, depending on the order he had been given; if he were told nothing, he remained seated, without lying down, until he finally fell asleep from exhaustion. On holidays, when *khorovody* were organized in the village, he did not normally participate; but if he were called to join the group and asked to sing, he sang; if he were asked to dance, he danced.

His father arranged a marriage for him, but marriage did not change the situation in any way; anyone who felt like it made fun of the poor idiot. He was so accustomed to that that only very rarely did the taunts and insults have the power to bother him. Having been repulsed and persecuted almost from the moment of his entry into the world, the idiot had voluntarily withdrawn into himself. He did not and had not the capacity to exert a will of his own; it could be said that he lived and moved propelled by the will of others. Yet —rarely, it is true—the idiot had ideas of his own. Thus, when springtime came, when the sun shone, the fields were green, and the trees covered with leaves anew, Fomushka headed for the woods and picked flowers, that he fastened to his cap, stuck in his belt, made into coronets or into big bouquets; and thus, loaded down with flowers, he returned to the village, his face radiant. At such times his habitual shyness and prickliness disappeared; if he encountered someone along the way, he smilingly offered the person a flower and said: "Take it; it comes from the woods."

This was the way Fomushka was, and the way he lived until the death of his father and his mother. After the death of the old man, Fomushka was shown the door by his wife, who went to work for strangers, and driven from the family home by his brothers. From then on, during the summer, he attached himself to the first family he found and worked and ate with them; but when autumn came and the work as a farmer was over, when the fields became bare and the clouds darkened, Fomushka went from village to village and, sometimes singing, sometimes dancing and miming, would be rewarded with a piece of bread, or a lodging, or a second-hand garment. Leading this kind of life, he lost a little of his timidity and lack of sociability and even occasionally was chatty and relaxed, although from time to time he was annoyed and suffered from the mockery to which he was subjected.

As a matter of fact, Fomushka was not a complete idiot; he was not utterly without intelligence, but he had not an alert and thoughtful mind such as is characteristic of the Russian people. Fomushka was too introspective, and was unable to express his thoughts as clearly and precisely as other persons were; yet it would be unjust to deny that he had intelligence. He was a creature born good, easygoing, and loving; but these natural qualities, finding themselves in constant conflict with the world around him, and continually being repulsed and repressed, had undermined and destroyed his morale. The indignities, teasing, insults, and affronts of which the poor creature was the target from his early years, at the hands both of his family and of strangers, inevitably caused an irreparable disturbance in his gentle, vulnerable psyche. Fomushka gave evidence of this disturbance primarily through his troubled eyes, his disordered thoughts, his incoherent speech, and in the alternating periods of long, stubborn silences and of sudden, childish garrulousness.

14

Fomushka approached the noisy group we have previously described.

"Look! Here comes the idiot; here is Fomushka."

"Fomouchka!" called someone who caught sight of him.

The noise and the singing stopped. In a moment everyone had surrounded the idiot.

"Hello, Fomushka! Hello, loony! Hello, Fomushka!" all of the voices called in chorus.

Fomouchka looked steadily at the group, shrugged his shoulders and replied: "Hello, hello, everybody!"

"What a beautiful dressing gown you are wearing, Fomushka!" said a young girl.

Fomushka silently gazed at his coverall and began to finger its frayed edges.

"And his cap, boy—what a gay dog he is!" observed another girl, bursting out laughing.

"Who made your *lapti?*" asked a third.

Fomushka looked at his footwear made of bark, hit it with his stick and responded: "I made them myself in the woods."

"Are you going to take a walk with us?" asked a fourth girl.

"How bored I was while you were absent, Fomushka! I was actually sick with longing!" exclaimed a fifth, who was greeted with a hearty and universal outburst of laughter.

"Yes, yes," added another voice. "Akulka told us she could die, she missed Fomushka so much."

"Look how elegantly he is dressed!" said a young boy, striking Fomushka's cap. The cap fell in the mud, and the laughter resumed. Fomushka smiled, but the smile was bitter and his heart was breaking. At the same time he had a vague realization that he was being humiliated, a feeling of futile resentment, and a childish fear of all people who were big, strong and witty; in other words, of everyone who was able to make fun of him. His lips trembled and his face clouded over, but this lasted only a second; then he became calm again, and his eyes regained their childish innocence. He picked up his mud-covered cap and put it on.

"Tell us, Fomushka, why you appear so sad today," demanded another boy. "Why are you such a stick in the mud? Sing us a song."

15

"Sing *Jourka*," said a young boy, coming forward.

"Sing! Sing!" the whole group ordered.

"No, definitely no," Fomushka said in a very strange tone of voice.

"Listen, Fomushka," Akulka put in. "I will sing, and you can do the bass." And she began to sing:

Is that you, Jourka! Jourka!
Jourka, the good man
Went off to the mill.
He witnessed a miracle:
A billy goat was making flour,
A nanny goat...

"What's the matter? You don't want to sing?"

"Why make him sing?" another girl asked. "The rest of us will sing, and Fomushka can dance."

"No, I don't want to," protested Fomushka.

"Ah, he doesn't want to! Dance anyway, Fomushka," they all chorused.

"Wait, Fomushka; I am going to dance with you," said Akulka.

"See, Akulka wants to dance with you," exclaimed the crowd.

Akulka advanced toward Fomushka, and the others positioned themselves around them. Then they all clapped their hands in rhythm to beat time to the dance. Akulka, posing her right hand on her hip and bending her head to the right, began to stamp her feet, slowly at first, then tapping them more and more quickly; finally, pressing her two fists against her sides, she bounded forward and leaped up, crying: "Now it's your turn; you can see what I am doing, can't you?" Fomushka began to move his feet, danced around Akulka two or three times and stopped. The singing ceased.

"What, fellow! Is that the way to dance? His partner has just begun her performance, and here he is already deserting her!"

These words were spoken by a traveling peddler who, unnoticed, had approached the group of dancers, letting his horse go on its way, accompanied by the monotonous sound of the bells hanging from his neck. The peddler was young and husky. He wore full trousers of black velvet, the bottoms tucked into the high tops of his boots, and a short fur-lined coat of some blue material, secured around his

waist by a red belt; a felt hat, circled by a band of velvet with a copper buckle, was tipped lightly over one ear. His dress and his manners indicated that he was an elegant and gallant traveling haberdasher.

"Good day, my beauties," he added, taking his pipe from his boot and lighting it. "Who is this handsome chap whom I see among you? How lucky he is! What a cluster of beauties crowd around him!"

Everyone burst out laughing. Fomushka pensively dug into the dirt with his stick.

A young girl responded: "Ah, friend trader, you are overcome with jealousy. You should know it is our village idiot."

"There is good reason to be jealous," said a boy.

"They wouldn't do as much for us. The idiot's in luck!" added another.

"See what a pretty dancing partner he's found," exclaimed several young girls, while the others laughed. Abruptly Fomushka roused himself and stopped his daydreaming.

"No," he said, "you are luckier than me. The idiot is miserable."

"Truthfully, are you lacking anything? Why, you are surrounded by beautiful girls, who are dancing and singing with you. Could anything be nicer?"

"Nice for the others, but sad for me," answered Fomushka. "You are much, much more fortunate. Everyone makes fun of the idiot; no one pities him."

"What about me, Fomushka? Don't I pity you?" asked Akulka. This was greeted with a new burst of laughter.

"No, it is true that no one shows any sympathy for him," one girl admitted. "But haven't you a wife?" she added.

"No," Fomushka replied. "She gave me the gate and is working for strangers."

"Ah," the peddler observed, "it seems clear to me that you didn't want to support her. So why did you get married?"

"My father wanted it and arranged the marriage."

"Your father wanted it," commented Akulka. "But tell me why you didn't marry Catherine."

The idiot let his head hang.

"Why are you bowing your head?" Akulka continued.

"Catherine was a good girl," Fomushka murmured, as if he were only talking to himself.

"Tell us why your father picked the wife he did," the peddler continued.

"Barbe was from our village; she had money but no suitors. She had a child, so my father made me marry her."

"Imagine that!"

The peddler burst out laughing, pushed his hat down more firmly on his head, and eyed the girls. Some were laughing, the others hiding behind their neighbors. Only one was choking back her laughter; she was a large girl with a red face, the youngest of all. Finally she too exploded noisily and, covering her face her hands, managed to cry: "The devil take you!" And she fled far away from the assembled group.

"Yoohoo!" a boy called after her.

Fomushka remained thoughtful and scratched the soil with his stick.

The peddler blew a puff of smoke out of his pipe and once more turned toward Fomushka.

"Catherine undoubtedly was very beautiful, wasn't she?"

Again Fomushka ceased his daydreaming and, as happened so often with him, went from taciturnity to garrulousness. "Catherine was good," he responded. "She pitied me. She never called me an idiot, but addressed me as Fomushka, and never insulted me. If I walked through the village and the children gathered around me, calling me names and harassing me, Catherine became aware of it and chased them away. See how dirty my shirt is now; once upon a time, Catherine would wash it for me. On holidays she combed my hair and put flowers on my cap. She even gave me a buckle—what a fine buckle!"

"Is it not the one that is still hanging from your shirt?" asked the peddler, indicating the fragments of a broken fastener.

The crowd laughed loudly.

"No,", said Fomushka. "I am holding onto that one; I keep it hidden. No one will ever again give me one like it."

"And where is your Catherine now?"

"They've taken her away; her husband has taken her away." He continued: "I went to the *izba*, where they were dancing and singing; it was very noisy... I wanted to join in—but there were children who pulled at me and cried out: "You've lost your fiancée. You've lost your fiancée!' I wanted to get rid of them. Catherine's husband came out, chased them off and said: "Go away!' I came back the next evening at nightfall, as I usually did. Catherine normally came out to go and fetch water, so I waited for her... Catherine did not come. The third day, still no Catherine; nor on the fourth day either. I never saw Catherine again, and my father arranged for me to marry."

Once more Fomushka fell into a reverie.

"Oh, you poor devil," said the peddler. He added: "Where is your father?"

"My father died last winter at Christmas time. Alas! It was very cold; the earth was frozen so solid that it could not be cut. I was obliged to dig his grave with an axe."

Night was falling. The peddler's horse was already making its presence known through the tinkling of its bells at the far end of the village.

"Ah, my wagon is far away. Farewell, my beauties," said the peddler. Then, giving Fomushka a copper *petak*, he lit his pipe and strode off toward his wagon.

The group of girls and boys broke up, and each individual went to his or her home, except for one fellow who kept circling Fomushka. "What have you in your hand?" he demanded.

Fomushka opened his hand and revealed his *petak*. The boy grabbed it and ran off as fast as he could.

"I've been robbed," shouted Fomushka, and he ran through the village.

It was now utterly dark, a cold fall night. The stars shone with a dull light. Throughout the village there was a profound silence; the villagers were all asleep. Only Fomushka did not fall asleep, as for a long time he contemplated the night. "How many stars..." he said. "One, two... one, two, three..." Thus did the village idiot count the stars until he slept, nevermore to awaken.

КУТИЛЫ

Поз. гес. М. 1859 г. 24 Апрелѣ Цензуръ И. Галеровъ Москва

Кутилы позднью порою,
Нанявши тройку лошадей,
Катятъ веселою гурьбою,
Лишь только слышенъ скрыпъ саней.

Но вотъ: съ цыганками лихими
Купцы-кутилы держатъ путъ
Усы заправивъ возжи въ руки
И вздернувъ шапку на бочекъ

Давно меня ждетъ Ямщика
И вотъ ямщикъ лихою трелью
Окресность шумно огласилъ
И словно громкою свирелью

The plague of Moscow

The year 1771 is etched in the memories of the inhabitants of Moscow as the most tragic period in the history of that city. "It was one year, or two years, before or after the plague," the old people still say today, dating everything from that terrible year, from that historical milestone. Even though approximately a century has passed since the frightful calamity swept through the city, in the ancient capital of the tsars the event is still mentioned with fright and, according to the most venerable citizens, was a disaster that can reasonably be compared to that of 1812... In 1771, it is true, Moscow was not set on fire, and no burning houses exposed smoky corpses to public view, but their appearance was no less sad to behold: the bolted doors, the windows closed off by planks nailed in place, the red crosses, true emblems of death, drawn on the fronts of those houses struck by the plague and stretching along both sides of the streets like two rows of huge tombs—all that was more fearful than the most fearful conflagration. Add to that the almost complete absence of any order or authority, the sepulchral silence of the outskirts and, in the center of the city, the furious cries of a populace in rebellion and thirsting for the blood of the very people striving to save them; also the looting of homes, the devastation of places of entertainment, and the stretchers with stinking corpses with which the maddened mob filled the streets and the squares. If one can picture this scene, one can realize that the calamity of 1771 indeed surpassed that of 1812.

The Asian plague, the *contagion,* that is the single word the people of Moscow still use to describe it, first made its appearance in Russia in 1770. At that time it raged in Moldavia, and Valachia, where our troops were stationed. It was the latter, presumably, who, through their frequent contacts with the inhabitants of Little Russia, first introduced it into the government offices at the frontier, whence it spread from one site to the other until it reached Moscow. At first the measures taken by the government seemed to have arrested it completely; but in the month of March of the following year, it flared up anew and spread so rapidly that by the month of September the number of deaths had risen to more than a thousand a day. All of the efforts to stem the violence and the progress of the outbreak were unavailing.

The people were indignant about the measures taken to save them, about the establishment of quarantine stations, about the closing of the public baths, and particularly about the prohibition against burying the dead in the cemeteries which at the time abutted the churches in the interior of the city. In troubled times it is always possible to encounter impostors eager to take advantage of the gullibility of the populace and to incite it to act irresponsibly. A clothing worker first spread the word among the population that, while asleep, he had had a heavenly vision, in which it had been revealed to him that the disaster that had struck the city of Moscow was caused by the fact that no one was chanting prayers and burning candles before the image of the Holy Virgin situated at the Varvarka gate. In spite of its absurdity, or rather precisely because it defied every rule of logic and common sense, this idea was enthusiastically embraced by the people, and they proceeded to rush *en masse* to the gate above which was incrusted, as is still the case today, the image of the Mother of God. Healthy persons and invalids alike came there from every part of Moscow, to pray continuously and to infect one another with the deadly virus that they carried back to their homes, which soon became the tombs of their entire families.

On September 15, during these days of mourning, a *telega* drawn by three horses slowly made its way along the Vladimir highway. In the *telega* was seated a merchant in a caftan of fine blue cloth, over which he wore a travel coat of Siberian fox. A first glance at his beard, as white as snow, and at his high and deeply wrinkled fore-head would have led one to judge him to be eighty years old. But the liveliness of his thoughtful and sometimes anxious gaze, his erect bearing and impressive stature and full cheeks, all of these things indicated that grief rather than years had etched the deep furrows on his brow and prematurely whitened his hair.

"Oh, the sun is making me warm," he said, removing his coat. "Eh, friend," he continued, turning to the coachman, "for miles now you have been going at a snail's pace. Isn't it time to trot a little?"

"Patience, master," the coachman replied. "Soon we'll arrive at a high point, after which we'll start to trot. But why are you in such a hurry? In these times, people are more apt to want to flee Moscow than to enter it."

"Is it a long time since you last visited Moscow?" asked the merchant.

"I was there five days ago. Then, too, I was driving a merchant from Rostow."

"Can you tell me if things are better there now?"

"Much better! The plague is raging, and everything is in a mess. They can't even find any more coffins."

"My God! My God!" murmured the merchant. "Do not punish me as I deserve for my sins!"

"We have angered the good Lord," continued the coachman. "But did you know, master, that the Holy Virgin is supposed to have appeared at the Varvarka gate?"

"I was not aware of it."

"When I made my last trip, like everyone else, I went there to light a candle to her. Lord, what a crowd was there; I mean what an enor-mous crowd! It was actually impossible to breathe. Yet it is reported that, in spite of that, more people are dying now than in the past."

"That is not surprising, my good man; the plague is a contagious malady. But I see we have at last reached the top of the hill," the merchant added. "Whip the horses, my boy!"

"Let's wait, master, until we have passed through this village. Look how much mud there is in the street. You really can't tell which way to turn."

The travelers had reached the village of Pouchkino. Some emaciated dogs were barking here and there, and calves which were dying of hunger wandered through the streets. Nowhere could a human voice be heard, and from no chimney did any smoke arise; everything was silent and dead, as if immobilized by Morpheus and black night.

"What does this mean, my friend?" asked the merchant. "Are people still asleep in their houses? Yet the sun is high in the sky."

"Asleep!" replied the coachman, shaking his head. "Everyone in Pouchkino is dead!"

"Is that possible? Everyone, you say?"

"My faith, yes, from the oldest to the youngest. There is not a living soul in this place."

"Everyone!" the merchant repeated to himself. Perhaps, three days ago, in that house over there, there was a father who loved his family, a mother embracing her children."

"Yes. And now," interrupted the coachman, who had overheard the words murmured in a low voice, "now there is no one to close the door. My colleague lived here; he was a rich peasant and the head of a family. What a charming family it was: ten sons, each one stronger and huskier than the last. Two weeks ago they were all in perfect health, but the last time I went through here I observed the old man, looking sick and beaten, seated alone on the earthen bench that was outside his *izba* (house). He tried to get up to say something to me, but he suddenly collapsed on the ground, sighed a great sigh, and there, before my very eyes, gave up the ghost."

The travelers had moved beyond most of the houses and were at the far end of the street that traversed the village when they caught sight of an old peasant woman, her head wrapped in a scarf, leaning out of the window, half of her body bending, foward, and seeming to be looking into the street.

"Thank the Lord!" exclaimed the merchant. "Here, finally, is one living soul."

The coachman shook his head.

"What! Are you blind?" protested the traveler, who had noticed the gesture. "Can't you see her there, in the last house?"

"I see her, master. But she has been looking out of the window for five days now. The poor woman! It seems that before dying she wanted to see the light that is the gift of God. Alas! Nobody was left to put her in the earth."

The merchant shuddered involuntarily and put his hand over his eyes when he passed in front of the *izba* where the disfigured corpse could be seen, the face covered with black spots and still bearing the traces of indescribable suffering.

After leaving the village, the coachman lashed his horses, and they broke into an easy gallop.

"A little faster still," the merchant ordered. "Otherwise we will not arrive before nightfall."

"Why go faster?" responded the coachman, shaking the reins. "Why be in such a hurry, master? It is clear that you are not bound for a picnic or a celebration."

"How do you know?" the merchant asked quickly.

"Who has a good time in Moscow today?"

"My wife and children are expecting me."

"Ah, that is different. But hold on a minute," the coachman went on, turning around toward the merchant. "Aren't you an inhabitant of Moscow named Theodore-Abramovitch Sibiriakoff?"

"Yes, that's me."

"Well, I said to myself that your voice was not unfamiliar. Yet I had a hard time recognizing you."

"How do you know me?"

"Was I not the one who, last fall, drove you and your whole family to Rostoff? Your house is in Varvarka, in the parish of Saint-Maxim-the-Confessor. A fine house, all built of stone, like a palace."

"That is so," responded the merchant. "And now I recognize you, too. Your name is Andrew, isn't it?"

"Yes, master, Andrew. I am also acquainted with your wife and children. As for your wife, there is no denying that she is a good and worthy woman; may the Lord grant her a long and healthy life! Your daughters, too, are beautiful and gracious. But your son..."

"I have no son."

"Then who was the little boy who was with you? A little redheaded brat who, if my recollection serves, you called Tereoshka."

"He is an adopted child."

"But why adopt a child when you have daughters of your own?"

"I adopted him at a time when I thought I would have no natural children."

"I understand. But if you will forgive my frankness, master, you acquired a child who leaves a great deal to be desired. That scamp of a Tereochka is an obvious bad egg. The practical joker!... Do you remember when we stopped at Great Barrier to let our horses have a breather? You all went to take tea, and I to have a glass of brandy, in the imperial tavern. What do you think that naughty redhead did during our absence? He unbridled all of the horses. Luckily, I came out just as he was finishing; otherwise... my horses are lively and would have ruined everything. I wanted to scold him, but the little devil picked up a stone and threw it at me so hard and with such good aim that he almost put my eye out."

"Yes," said the merchant, with a sigh, "yes, heaven has punished me by inflicting this child on me."

"But, master, why not show him the door? Is he related to you?"

"Not at all. But since the Lord has not abandoned me, in spite of my sins, how can I abandon this unfortunate and penniless orphan? Undoubtedly he will cause me further grief, I expect that, but what can I do? Apparently it was the will of God that I be punished, and as long as he spares my wife and children..."

"Take heart, master," the coachman said. "Perhaps everything is not lost. God is good!... But now the road is becoming as smooth as silk. Can we gallop for a little while?"

"Please. Try to arrive in Moscow in time for mass, and you'll have a tip of a ruble."

"Thank you, master! I hope that your carriage is solid," added the coachman, gathering the reins together. "Go, my hearties. Sit tight, Theodore-Abramovitch," he continued, taking from his belt a whip with a short handle and a long whiplash. "Wake up, gray! Do your feet hurt? Get a move on! Go!"

And with the plucky coachman calling to the horses to urge them on, the *telega* took off like a flash of lightning. The travelers whizzed by villages and hamlets as if shot out of a gun, and when the coachman managed with some difficulty to arrest his horses, carried away by the excitement of the dash, and stopped near the cross at the barrier of Troitsa, the mass had not yet begun. An old pensioner came forward and approached the carriage, looking sullen. When he learned that the merchant came from the *fortunate village of Iaroslaw,* he opened the barrier without further questions.

The travelers had barely cleared the barrier when, in front of them, at the end of the street, a hoarse alcoholic voice resounded: "Make way there! Make way! The *gentlemen* have arrived!"

In the twinkling of an eye the centre of the street was empty, and Theodore-Abramovitch saw such a terrible funeral procession coming that his heart froze in fear. Along the side of the barrier there advanced a long line of wagons loaded down with coffins. Some of these coffins were so imperfectly nailed together that the planks were loosely joined, and it seemed as if they were going to break open with every bump of the wagons; others were simple packing cases without covers, and with each movement of the wagons one could see the corpses, partially enveloped in worn mats, budge. The live persons who accompanied this funeral procession were perhaps even more frightful than the dead, not because of their tunics and their caps of oilcloth, that made them resemble ghosts, but because of their drunkenness, their repulsive faces, their fierce looks, and their crazy laughter at the sight of the passers-by who hurried away to let them through. They could truly be described as demons. They were followed, some distance behind, by soldiers of the garrison, under the command of an officer on horseback.

"Good Lord!" the merchant exclaimed. "Who are these people? They do not even look human."

"Can't you see that they have irons on their feet?" the coachman asked. "They are convicts."

"Convicts!" the merchant repeated with emotion.

"Yes. In the beginning the undertakers saw to the burials, but they were all wiped out by the plague, and now they are obliged to depend upon the prisoners."

One of the latter approached Theodore-Abramovitch, holding out a sort of cash box. "Won't you give something," he asked, "in memory of the dead?"

"Come on, don't be stingy," added another. "Tomorrow, perhaps it will be your turn, and we'll be carrying you."

The merchant threw them a fistful of small coins, which they fell upon and fought over like starving dogs. One alone among them, a giant seven feet tall, did not take part in the melee, but remained where he was, motionless, studying the merchant very attentively.

"Well, Sky High, what have you got to gape at?" demanded one of his companions in chains. "Do you want someone to rub your shoulders? Forward march!"

"Let's get away from here quickly," the merchant said to the coachman. "The sight of these men sickens me."

"You'll get used to it in a day or two," answered the coachman, whipping his horses.

They went from the barrier to the Soukhareff tower without encountering a single soul. The only interruptions in the deathly silence, that came at rare intervals, were low moans and groans issuing from scattered houses. These, plus the church cemeteries, the corpses of indigent dead that had no graves, closed doors, windows with broken panes, red crosses on all of the houses—this was the scene that greeted them in the suburb of Meshchanskaya. Beyond the Soukhareff Tower, in the city properly speaking, our voyagers laid eyes first on a few individuals who were by themselves, then on groups of men and women whom they overtook and passed. But once they arrived at the Nikolskaïa Gate, to the left, along the ramparts, they had to stop at almost every step so as not to crush the dense crowd.

"The explanation, master," said the coachman, "is that they all have come to pray to the image of Varvarka. See how many are there! And there! And look down there near the gate; what a seething mass! It's as if a caldron were boiling over."

"Listen and tell me what that is," said the merchant, straining to hear an indistinct noise that, like distant claps of thunder, rose from the immense mob crowding around the image of the Holy

Virgin. "That is not simply the sound of thunder... Do you hear those cries?"

"I hear them. The last time there were fewer people, and they did not cry as loudly. Are the people from the factories not over there?"

"The Lord preserve us!"

"Master, if you are willing to draw a little nearer, you will be able to see better."

The travelers moved forward, but when they were about three hundred paces from the Varvarka gate, they were forced to come to a complete stop, for the entire area that extended from the ramparts to the church of All-Saints was closely packed with people.

"It is impossible to advance any farther," Theodore-Abramovitch told the coachman, at the same time getting out of the *telega*. "Go, and take the route that passes by the Ilinka gate; I will walk to the house."

The coachman turned the carriage around, and the merchant elbowed through the crowd, sometimes pushed back and sometimes pushed forward, until he was at the foot of the wall to which the image of the Holy Virgin was fastened. The sight that struck him first was that of a little man with frizzy hair, in rags, dirty, and looking like a criminal who had just escaped from prison, who was standing on a bench and from time to time called out in a shrill voice: "Put your candles here and win atonement from the Mother of God!" So people could reach the image, that was two *sazhens* (twelve feet) above the ground, a ladder had been placed along the wall, and the crowd ascended it without any letup. Some kissed the icon, and others lit candles in front of it. Those below hung onto the garments of those preceding them on the rungs, pulling them back and frequently tumbling with them to the ground, where they trampled them underfoot and were themselves trampled by those above them. Curses, moans, the crying of women and the sighs of the dying, all were drowned out by the low, deep murmur rising from the mob, that rumbled and roared like a rough sea. As he could not help overhearing certain conversations, he was brought up short by the mention of the archbishop Ambrose, and understood, by certain observed gestures, that the holy prelate was in great danger. Desiring to find out in more detail just what sort of peril menaced the

29

man, he posed several questions to those around him. The responses were either vague or else provided useless information that he considered unworthy of attention.

When the crowd became a little less dense, Theodore-Abramovitch headed for his house. When he reached the elevation on which stood the church of Saint George, he found the place completely deserted. Behind him rose the noise from the area he had just left; in front of him, the street was empty. The only sign of life was in the windows of some of the houses of wealthy merchants, where women who had secluded themselves inside and did not dare go out made furtive appearances. Suddenly the merchant, who was taking great strides, stopped, for he saw in the distance the roof of his house. Until that moment he had not been altogether unhappy; he had been able to think and to tell himself: "I am going to be reunited with my wife and children." But now he suddenly realized that in one more minute, after taking one more step, he might conceivably learn that he was alone in the world, an orphan with white hair; perhaps he might even search without finding them for the tombstones over which he might at least weep. "Lord of mercy," murmured the unhappy old man, "I have no right to ask for any favors, but if it will help redeem their lives, make me endure sickness and suffering, make me descend alive into the grave, and I will proclaim that You are kind and merciful."

Just at that moment a small boy, homely of face and with his clothes in disorder, who was running and constantly looking behind him, bumped into the merchant.

"Tereochka!" the latter exclaimed, stopping him. "It is you!"

"Certainly it is me," said the lad, attempting to free himself.

"Wait a minute. Where are you running? Tell me, is everything all right at the house? My wife, my daughters..."

"What's that to me?" the rascal responded insolently, looking impatiently in the direction of Varvarka.

"They are still alive, aren't they?"

"How would I know?"

"But aren't you still living with them?"

"Gosh, no! They slapped me around too much there... Now let go of me!"

"Is it possible," responded the merchant, "that you have actually left my household? How did you dare?"

"This is how I dared," retorted the youth, wrenching himself free from the hands of his adoptive father and running as fast as his legs could carry him toward the tumultuous crowd.

"He is alive, at least," murmured Theodore-Abramovitch, his gaze following his protégé, "but perhaps those unrecognized angels, my wife and my daughters... Oh, gives wings to my feet. What will be will be, but the uncertainty is killing me."

Soon he was at the threshold of his house. He looked: the shutters were closed, the door to the street blocked off by boards. "Good Lord! There is a red cross, but perhaps..." As a matter of fact, a dog was barking in the courtyard; the house was not entirely deserted. The merchant knocked. No response, except by the dog, who had recognized his master and barked louder than ever. A few minutes passed; the deathly silence continued. But a window in the next house opened slowly, and a man with a pale and drawn face said to the merchant: "Don't knock, friend; there's no one in that house."

"No one," the merchant repeated with a catch in his voice. "But the mistress..."

"Died three days ago."

"And her daughters?"

"The last one was taken to the cemetery yesterday."

"The last!" muttered the unhappy father. And he leaned against the wall of his house.

The merchant did not go out of his mind: he realized and under-situations in a person's life that we describe as painful but which, as a matter of fact, cannot really be described in any words known in as a matter of fact, cannot really described in any words known in any language. The feeling they engender is as intense and as brief as the last rale of a dying man; yet a life filled with torment and a century of agony would be as nothing compared to such torture of the soul. The old man did not utter a single word; not a single tear fell from his eyes; not a single sigh rose from his chest. He looked at the sky; the sky was a brilliant, unclouded blue, but as mute and dead as his own heart. It seemed to him that someone was whispering in his ear: "Do not knock there, either; no one will answer you." The merchant's desolate gaze turned toward the doorway of the church in front of which he was standing, and he was seized with an access of furious despair. "So, oh God," he cried out, "neither my repentance, nor my heartfelt prayers, nor my tears born in blood have been able to assuage Your wrath!" At that moment someone came out. A service was going on; through the half-open door, Theodore-Abramovitch could hear the gentle voices of the priests. They were chanting: "Glory to God, the king of heaven, who brings consolation to men's souls!" The curse words and outcries of despair died before they could leave the merchant's lips; peace entered his heart like a soft rain after a storm, while tears flowed from his eyes and comforted him. He knelt and bent beneath the hand of the Lord, that touched him. A personal prayer relieved his soul. Certainly he continued to suffer from the loss he had just experienced and could say: "My soul is sad unto death," but he no longer denounced Him who gives and who takes away. "Let Your will be done!" he repeated, fixing his eyes on the image of the Savior placed close to the doorway.

His reverie was interrupted by the sound of a crowd of men who were ascending from Varvarka toward the center of the city, and he heard the name of the archbishop Ambrose pronounced by some in the group. The merchant shuddered and trembled, fearful for the life of the prelate, whom he knew personally. Convinced that the mob's bloodthirsty plans were real and dangerous, Theodore-Abramovitch resolved to thwart them if it was at all possible.

Therefore the next day, September 16, early in the morning he sped to the monastery of Donskoï, where Ambrose was then staying. At the door of the monastery he encountered a young novice and the prelate's valet and urgently pleaded with them to persuade the archbishop to take refuge far from Moscow without delay. Ambrose was willing to take this advice, but the assassins arrived at the site before he had time to quit the monastery. Since it was impossible to escape, he sought haven in the church. The assassins followed him there, and it was Tereochka, the merchant's adopted son, who discovered him in the choir loft and delivered him to their superstitious rage.

As we know, Ambrose had wanted to remove the icon that was attracting to the Varvarka gate an assemblage whose members were being infected by fatally contagious germs, even while they believed they were being protected from them.

The assassins dragged the archbishop in front of the iconostasis, and one of them, whom Theodore-Abramovitch recognized as the workman with frizzy hair who, at the Varvarka gate, had been collecting money for expiatory candles to be burned before the image of the Holy Virgin, rushed at the prelate to inflict final punishment. After hurling reproaches and insults at him, he thrust a large knife toward him and was about to plunge it into his chest when the merchant, who had followed the assassins, seized his arm and held him back.

"Why is the merchant getting mixed up in this?" roared the assassins. "Kill him! Kill him!"

"But, my friends, am I not one of you?" asked Theodore-Abramovitch, who was pretending to be a member of their mob in order to be able to influence them. "Is this the place for such an execution? Let us not desecrate the Lord's church. Rather let us take this man outside the sanctuary; then we can question him and decide what to do."

The merchant hoped that, by gaining time, he might succeed in curbing the mob's fury and helping the prelate escape, but his efforts were in vain. Ambrose was killed, but his murderers soon paid for their crime. Hieropkine, the governor of Moscow, managed to mobilize several companies of the regiment of Velikolutsky, camped twenty miles from the city, and, with the aid of this handful of men, broke up the band of outlaws and captured the assassins. Thanks to his initiative, order returned to the ancient capital of the tsars, where eventually the plague decreased in violence and its devastation came to an end.

Ukrainian tale

"Oh, Mommy, how unhappy I am! I ask you, is there anywhere in the world a person as unhappy as me?"

"Tell me what has happened to you, my poor child."

"Oh, dear me, dear me, how unhappy I am!" repeated Annouchka, sobbing.

"My poor heart, my little dove, my little pigeon, I beg you to tell your old mother what has happened."

"Oh, dear me, dear me. How unhappy I am! I went for a walk along the bank of the river, and I met a fortune teller who read my palm. She told me that I was going to get married, that I would have a child, that at that time I would be living on the other side of the brook, that my child would want to go all by himself to visit his grandmother, that he would try to cross the river and that he would be drowned."

"Good grief, good grief! My poor child, how unlucky we both are!"

And the two women entered the *izba*, crying in their aprons.

At the sound of their weeping, Annushka's sister joined them.

"My God, what has happened?"

"Oh, my poor child," her mother replied, "how unhappy we are! Your sister went for a walk along the river bank and met a fortune teller who read her palm. The witch told her that she would soon get married, that she would have a child, that she would go to live on the other side of the river, that her child would want to go all by himself to visit his grandmother, that he would fall in the water and be drowned."

And the three women began to moan and groan in chorus.

Yegor, the oldest of the children, returned from the fields just at that moment.

"What's the matter; what's happened?"

The three women all answered at once:

"Oh, my God, my God, how unhappy we are!"

The mother went on:

"Your sister decided to go for a walk along the river bank. She met a fortune teller who read her palm and predicted that she soon was going to marry, that she would have a child, that she would then go to live on the other side of the stream, that her little boy would want to come all by himself to see his good old grandmother, that he would fall into the water and that he would be drowned!"

At that the brother added his voice to theirs; now they were four to cry and to moan.

The father came back in his turn.

"What's the matter? What's happened?"

"A great misfortune, little Father, a very great misfortune indeed!"

And all of them simultaneously began to tell him the tale of Annushka's misadventure.

Whereupon the father became furiously angry.

"You are unbelievably stupid, to be so grief-stricken because of the foolish predictions of an old hag! I am going to lock you all up in the barn, and I will not set you free until or unless I meet someone even more stupid than you!"

And the father locked them up, put the key in his pocket, and walked off in search of adventure.

He walked for a long time, or perhaps not so long, until he

arrived at an isolated house in the middle of some fields. He saw a peasant straddling the roof and pulling with all his might on a cord. Ivan Alexandrovitch, which was the name of Annushka's father, walked around the house, which concealed from him the objective of the peasant's efforts, and saw a superb black cow—that the good man perched on the roof was pulling as hard as he could by the neck, at the risk of strangling her.

"What on earth are you doing?" Ivan called to the peasant.

"You can see, little Father, that I am trying to raise the cow to the roof."

"That is certainly what I can see," replied Ivan, "but, apart from the fact that it would be as impossible to succeed as to hold water in a bottomless pail, of what possible use would the act be?"

"Don't you understand anything then, old devil? Don't you see that grass has grown on my roof, and if I can manage to lift the cow up there, I won't have to take the trouble to use my sickle and cut it?"

"Bless me," Ivan said to himself, shrugging his shoulders, "here is someone as stupid as my whole family put together. But perhaps I may be able to find someone who goes him one better."

And Ivan continued on his way. He walked for another long interval, until he arrived at a fine and prosperous-looking farm. In the courtyard, an enormous sow was frolicking with her little ones. A maid servant with a stupid expression was at a window of the house.

Ivan entered the courtyard and, taking off his cap, headed toward the sow, to which he bowed low and said:

"Good day, little Aunt. We are having a little family reunion at the house, and I have come to invite you to attend."

"What is the matter?"

"Mistress, there is a man in the courtyard who calls our big sow his aunt and has just invited her to attend a little family reunion."

The farmer's wife thought for a while, then observed: "After all, the sow was not born here; we bought her at the market. We do not know where she came from."

So the good woman went to the window and asked:

"Our sow is your aunt?"

"Without a doubt, since I am her nephew."

"Oh. And you want to take her with you to attend a little family reunion?"

"Yes indeed."

"Do you live far away?"

"Yes, quite a distance."

"Then the poor animal will never be able to follow you with her seven little ones. Wait. I am going to lend you a wagon and our white horse, so that you can transport her more comfortably."

Ivan thanked her profusely.

The farmer's wife had the white horse harnessed, helped Ivan load the sow and her seven little ones into the wagon, and Ivan Alexandrovitch departed, snapping his whip.

The weather was magnificent, and Ivan, in a good humor, sang a marching song he had learned in the regiment when he served in Kazan:

> Vdol da po rechkye
> Rechkye po Kazankye
> Chorny selezien plyviot
> Vdol da po berezhku
> Vdol da po krutomu
> Dobry molodiets idyot.

The sow and her little ones accompanied him as he sang. But he soon interrupted the tune, for he heard, far behind him, the sound of a galloping horse. And the shrewd peasant surmised that the farmer who owned the sow, and who had been absent at the time of his visit, must have returned and now be pursuing him.

Ivan Alexandrovitch of Poltava jumped from his seat, took the horse by the reins, and hid the wagons and its passengers in a stand of birch trees next to the side of the road. Then he returned to the highway, took off his cap, filled it with earth, put a cloth over it and waited.

The noise drew nearer. Soon a rider came into sight, gesturing furiously.

He stopped his horse short in front of Ivan, who stood motionless.

"Have you seen a white horse pass, pulling a wagon containing a sow and her seven little ones?"

"I would be blind if I had not seen it," responded Ivan.

"And do you know which way the son of a gun who was driving it went?"

"I know not only which way he went, but I also know where he lives."

"You know where he lives? Go after him as fast as you can and bring him to me, alive or dead!"

"I would like to, good little Father," replied Ivan, "but what sort of reception do you think they would give a poor peasant, so poorly dressed? How could they trust me enough to hand over a horse, a wagon, a sow and her seven little ones? Oh, if I only had a fine caftan like yours!"

"That's no problems; I'll lend you my caftan!"

"And besides, how can I catch your thief, who can go much more quickly in a wagon than I'll be able to on foot?"

"Take my horse; he'a good solid animal."

"And lastly, kind sir, you need to lend me your cap. With these fine clothes and this elegantly caparisoned mount, I shouldn't be bareheaded. And in my cap I have a nest of young eagles that I have just captured in the forest and that I will not give up for any amount of money."

"Here is my headpiece; I will keep a careful watch on yours until you return."

And Ivan Alexandrovitch of Poltava went galloping off. He returned to the forest by a different road, harnessed the farmer's black horse alongside the white horse and returned triumphantly to his home, snapping his whip. He descended from his wagon, unharnessed the horses, put them in the stable, put the sow and her little ones in the pigpen, took the key from his pocket and opened the door to the barn, saying to his family:

"You can come out now; I have found someone more stupid than you."

Story of the green lizard, the gray squirrel and the eagle

Once upon a time there lived a tsar, Vasili Fyodorovitch. This tsar had two passions: his daughter Helena, as beautiful as day and as dark as night; and archery, that he considered the only occupation worthy of a nobleman. Therefore his ministers and his favorites were selected from among the best archers in the realm.

When the young princess became of marriageable age, Tsar Vasili Fyodorovitch decreed that only the most skillful archer deserved to be his son-in-law.

And heralds proclaimed throughout the city:

"Tsar Vasili Fyodorovitch, our revered ruler and our benevolent lord, will give his daughter, the radiant Princess Helena, to the best archer of the realm. And there will be a great archery competition to which are invited all the loyal subjects of the tsar, our venerated father."

"The competitors are ordered to enter on horseback, with a single arrow in their quiver and, without descending from their horses and without stopping their mounts, to shoot their arrows at the target, that will be so far away that it will be hard to see.

"Those who fail to hit the target will be beheaded."

And do you know how many competitors entered the lists?

Only three, even though at stake was the hand of the radiant Princess Helena. On the other hand, those who missed the target would lose their heads.

And the tsar, Vasili Fyodorovitch, always kept his promises, especially promises of this sort.

Thus three contestants entered the competition.

The first, one of the wealthiest and most powerful lords of the realm, was mounted on a black horse.

The second was a young and handsome lord with a soft, appealing gaze, crimson lips, and a thin black mustache. He was clad in magnificent clothing of gold cloth embroidered with small pearls. And his horse was as white as snow.

The third ...oh, the third did not wear magnificent clothing; he wore a peasant blouse and poor trousers of a printed material such as peddlers sell at country fairs.

His horse was not rigged out like those of his rivals; a sheepskin served as a saddle, and a simple rope masqueraded as a rein.

And when the little peasant, timid and frail, with blond hair and blue eyes, appeared in this outfit, the tsar burst out laughing, laughing boisterously. All of the courtiers laughed until they cried, the royal guards followed suit, while the army and the crowd and everyone else also laughed and laughed, until the whole field was swept by one enormous outburst of laughter.

But the daughter of the tsar, the beautiful Helena, did not laugh. She had noticed how the eyes of the young peasant shone, limpid and as deeply blue as the Ukrainian sky after a summer rain, how his hair was golden like ripe wheat, how his figure was supple like the great poplars on the hill; and she had thought that it required a great deal of courage for the little peasant thus to confront the best archers of the realm...

At a signal from the tsar, the tourney began. The distinguished lord saluted the tsar and his daughter, urged his horse forward and, without slowing down its pace, almost without looking, sent his arrow straight at the target, far away as it was.

Applause rang out from every side. And the distinguished lord proudly took his place near the royal box.

The young nobleman with the soft eyes, the crimson lips, and the suit of cloth of gold embroidered with pearls, started off at a brisk pace and, without checking his mount or diminishing its speed, almost without looking at the target, sent his arrow straight toward it, far away and difficult to hit as it was.

Applause rang out anew, and the first arrogant lord grew pale with chagrin and fear. His happy rival took a position alongside him.

It was the turn of Ivan, the young peasant; instead of heading in the direction of the target, he set off in the opposite direction in a burst of speed.

"Oh, the miserable wretch!" said the tsar. "Look at him trying to save his head! I command you to bring him back."

He had barely issued the order when Ivan could be seen returning at a gallop on his roan colt, passing like a flash of lightning in front of the royal box and, almost without looking, sending his arrow straight at the target, straight at the distant goal.

Now the applause became frenzied, and all of the people roared and jumped for joy at the success of one of their own, at the triumph of the peasant over the fine nobles clothed in gold.

Ivan got down from his horse and presented himself to the tsar.

"Give me your daughter, sire, as you have sworn to do."

Tsar Vasili Fyodorovitch was overcome by an access of fury and cried out wrathfully:

"Vile peasant, how do you dare aspire to have the hand of the daughter of the tsar, the hand of the beautiful Princess Helena, who is more beautiful than the day, darker than the night? Consider yourself fortunate that your skill has saved your life and that I am not punishing you for your impudence. But, nevertheless, I will agree to give you my daughter if you bring me the ring of the tsar, Viazma, my enemy; however, only then will I give you my daughter, Princess Helena, beautiful as the day, dark as the night."

Ivan left with a heavy heart. And the crowd silently gave way to let him pass, as people withdraw before a funeral procession.

Ivan departed from the village, very sad and his heart very heavy;

he followed roads and highways, crossed plains and climbed mountains. He rode for three days and finally arrived at the edge of a forest; he was hungry and thirsty and tired. He fastened his horse to a tree and looked around him, searching for something to eat. Suddenly he spied a shrub on which were three small golden apples, that shone with a marvelous brilliance.

This tree was an enchanted tree that produced fruit only once every hundred years. And he who found the tree and ate of its fruit would fall into a deep sleep; upon awaking, he would be able to understand the language of the animals of the forest who, from that time on, would be devoted to him. Ivan ate the fruit of the enchanted tree, and its taste was delicious. He had barely finished eating when he fell into a deep sleep.

He slept for a long time; on awaking and opening his eyes, Ivan saw near him a pretty green lizard, standing on its hind legs and gazing at him affectionately. The lizard, seeing he was awake, asked:

"Did you sleep well, Ivan?"

"Oh, yes," replied Ivan, amazed that he could understand the language of the green lizard.

"You are distressed about something? I heard you groan and sob in your sleep. What can I do for you? You have eaten the three golden apples; you are the friend of the animals in the forest."

"Alas!" Ivan sighed. "As a matter of fact, I am very distressed, for I am in love with the daughter of Tsar Vasili Fyodorovitch, who is beautiful as the day, dark as the night; how I love her!... I won the archery contest, and the king had promised her to the winner. But now he has imposed an impossible condition before I can marry her. I have to bring him the ring of Tsar Viazma, his enemy. And I am certain to perish in the attempt!"

"Ivan, Ivan, if you, a humble peasant, had never presumed to cast your eyes on a princess, you would not be in such distress today. However, do not despair. I can help you; wait three days for me, and I will bring you the ring of Tsar Viazma."

And the green lizard disappeared. Three days passed, and the green lizard returned; the gold ring of Tsar Viazma gleamed in his little mouth.

Ivan gave a great cry of joy, thanked his good friend the green lizard, affectionately clasped his little paws in his own hand, and leaped onto his horse.

He rode for three days and three nights; he followed roads and highways, crossed plains and climbed mountains.

"Sire, here is the gold ring of Tsar Viazma, your enemy. Give me your daughter as you have promised."

"You have performed an outstanding feat, my boy, and if you bring me the gold goblet that is used by Tsar Ryashchuk, my rival, I will assuredly give you my daughter."

So Ivan left the village, very sad and heavy-hearted; he followed roads and highways and climbed mountains. He rode for three days and three nights, and finally arrived at the edge of the forest.

The lizard came to meet him.

"You have come back? And I do not see an expression of great joy on your face. Does that mean that you have not wed the daughter of Tsar Vasili Fyodorovitch?"

"Alas! Alas! If I do not bring back the gold goblet that belongs to Tsar Ryashchuk, who reigns yonder on the other side of the forest, the king will refuse to give me the hand of Helena, who is beautiful as the day, dark as the night. I am going to attempt the exploit, but surely I will perish in the attempt!"

"Ivan, if you had remained in your cottage, if you had never cast your eyes on the beautiful Helena, you would not be in such distress today. However, I am going to try to get you out of your predicament. Are you not the friend of the denizens of the forest?"

And the green lizard called to "Little Gray" and told him of Ivan's problem.

"Do not be discouraged," said the squirrel. "I know Tsar Ryashchuk; after his noonday repast, he settles down in his garden beneath a huge oak tree to enjoy some mead drunk from his gold goblet. Then he goes to sleep. I will go there and keep an eye on him from the branches of the oak; while he is asleep, I will steal the goblet from him and bring it back to you. Are you not the friend of the denizens of the forest? Wait three days for me..."

Three days passed. The squirrel returned, holding the precious goblet in front of him between his paws; and Ivan thanked his

45

friends and leaped on his horse.

He rode three days, he rode three nights, he followed roads and highways, he climbed mountains.

"Sire, here is the goblet of Tsar Ryashchuk, your rival? Now are you willing to give me your daughter?"

"You have certainly demonstrated admirable valor and skill, and if you bring me the head of Kara-Karta-Khan, the redoutable chief of the Tartars, I will give you my daughter; I give you my solemn oath."

So Ivan left the village, very sad and heavy-hearted. He followed roads and highways, crossed plains and climbed mountains. He rode for three days and three nights and finally arrived at the edge of the forest. His friend the green lizard came to meet him and asked:

"How does it happen that you are back here, sad-faced and still dressed in your peasant's clothes? Does it mean that you have not yet married the daughter of Tsar Vasili Fyodorovitch? What is the reason that you are even sadder than the last time you were here?"

"Alas! Alas! There is no longer any hope for me. Tsar Vasili Fyodorovitch still refuses to give me his daughter, the beautiful Helena, beautiful as the day, dark as the night. Before he will give me her hand, he wants me to bring him the head of Kara-Kharta-Khan, the redoutable Tartar chieftain who reigns yonder, on the other side of the great river."

"Ivan, Ivan, if you had remained in your village, if you had not cast your eyes on the daughter of the tsar, the beautiful Helena, you would not have been so unhappy today. Yet I am going to try to come to your assistance once again. Are you not the friend of the denizens of the forest?" And the green lizard called to the eagle, the dean of the forest, and informed him about Ivan's difficulties.

The old eagle reflected for a long time, then said:

"Do you not realize that it is impossible to succeed in such an enterprise if you do not possess the enchanted sword?"

"The enchanted sword?"

"The enchanted sword, that makes the one who draws it from its scabbard invisible. It is guarded yonder, in the plain of bones, by a giant who stands watch over it day and night. Get up on my back,

46

and I will carry you there."

Ivan climbed onto the eagle's back, and the eagle immediately soared aloft. He flew over plains and mountains, over brooks and rivers.

At the end of three days, they arrived at the Plain of Bones.

It was night. The immense plain was strewn with skeletons, the skeletons of those who had attempted to overcome the enchanted sword.

The sword was placed on a granite pedestal. The giant was seated nearby. A log was burning and caused the jewels that ornamented the scabbard of the mysterious blade to glitter.

The eagle gently put Ivan down behind a rock and told him: "I am going to hurl myself at the giant and claw his eyes out. While I am thus engaged, you will take possession of the sword and will come back here quickly to wait for me."

The eagle clawed out the giant's eyes, as the giant uttered frightful screams. Ivan took possession of the sword, rejoined his friend behind the rock and once more mounted on his back.

The eagle took flight and was soon within view of the camp of the Tartars; he put Ivan down in a nearby forest.

Ivan girded on the sword and walked toward the camp of Kara-Karta-Khan; it was black night.

Only Khan's tent still showed a light; Ivan drew the sword from its scabbard and became invisible. In spite of the sentinels, he was able to enter into the camp, since they could not see him; thus he arrived at the entrance to the tent of Kara-Karta-Khan. Guards were sleeping lengthwise across the door; Ivan, always invisible, entered the tent. Kara-Karta-Khan was sound asleep; with a single slash of the enchanted sword, Ivan cut off his head. Once more he stepped over the bodies of the sleeping guards; blood dripped over one of the soldiers, who awoke with a start.

"It is raining," he said, "and yet there is not a cloud in the sky." And the warrior turned over heavily and went back to sleep.

Ivan found his friend the eagle in the forest and once more mounted on his back; they soared over plains and mountains, rivers and streams, and at last Ivan again found himself at the edge of the dark forest.

He thanked his good friends, fastened the head of Kara-Karta-Khan to his saddle and set forth. He followed roads and highways, crossed plains and climbed mountains, and finally arrived at the gates of the city.

"What is the matter? Why is someone disturbing my sleep? Why these outcries? What has happened, that such a crowd is gathered at the gates of the city? Why are all of my people shouting so loudly and so joyously?"

"Sire, Ivan the peasant has arrived, carrying on his saddle the head of Kara-Karta-Khan, the redoutable chief of the Tartars!"

At that, Tsar Vasili Fyodorovitch dressed hastily and descended the stairs of the palace. Just at that instant Ivan arrived and threw at his feet the head of Kara-Karta-Khan. And the tsar took Ivan in his arms, clasped him to his heart in a tender embrace and called him his beloved son.

The wedding took place three days later, the wedding of the beautiful Helena, beautiful as the day, dark as the night, and of Ivan, the humble peasant!

The celebration lasted for three weeks, and the guests departed laden with valuable gifts. Eventually the young couple had three children: two girls and a boy.

The oldest was a boy, or perhaps it was a girl; I am not sure about that!...

Ruslan and Chernomor

The beautiful Olga, the daughter of Ivan, the grand duke of Kiev, his cherished daughter, had disappeared; no one knew what had become of her, and everyone was grief-stricken. For Olga, the cherished daughter of the grand duke Ivan, was as good as she was beautiful.

Among the grief-stricken were three knights, all three of them in love with the beautiful girl, all three eager to marry her.

Tsar Ivan ordered the three knights to appear before him and told them:

"I have summoned all three of you here because you love my daughter, and I have just learned what has become of her."

"Tell us, noble lord, what has become of the princess!"

"Alas! Alas! She has been kidnapped by Chernomor, the sorcerer of the accursed mountain, and I am unspeakably sorrowful, for I am also aware of the fate awaiting my poor child, a fate similar to the fate of all the women who have refused Chernomor. A fortune teller has revealed everything to me. Chernomor lives on the accursed mountain in a castle in the midst of a dense forest. It is there that he has brought my daughter to make her his wife. And as she has certainly refused, she must have undergone the same misfortune as all of the other young women who have preceded her in the accursed castle!"

"And what fate did these young girls suffer, noble lord?"

"The sorcerer carries in his belt a magic net that was given him by the devil. As soon as he throws this net over the victim he has selected, she becomes a goldfish. His fish pond is already very well stocked, and I have reason to fear that my daughter may have joined the monster's other victims."

"And what do you ask of us, noble lord, our Father? Whatever you order us to do, we shall do our best to carry out your wishes."

"All three of you are to leave for the accursed castle and avenge the princess or perish!"

Then Ruslan, a wise and valiant knight, said to the tsar: "I will avenge the princess and free her, or I will die in the act!"

Ratmir the dreamer, Ratmir the poet, Ratmir the absent-minded, took up the refrain. "We will avenge her or perish!"

And Farlaff, Farlaff the coward, repeated tremblingly: "We will avenge her or perish!"

But he had great difficulty concealing the panic he was feeling at the thought of taking such a dangerous risk!

The first to leave was Ratmir the dreamer, Ratmir the poet, Ratmir the absent-minded.

He had gone scarcely a hundred paces outside the city when he met a shepherdess guarding her sheep. And now Ratmir, finding the girl attractive, got down from his horse and began wooing her with honeyed words.

Princess Olga, his mission, his vow were all forgotten!

The next to leave was Farlaff the coward, who had gone scarcely a hundred paces into the forest when he took to his heels!

Ruslan the valiant had not yet departed! On the contrary, he had closeted himself in his home, and had had brought to him rich materials, valuable jewels, cosmetics and ointments. He had clothed himself in a woman's attire, had made up his face and was posing and making faces in front of the mirror.

50

How foolish!... Or how shrewd?

In Chernomor's fish pond were handsome goldfish that had once been the most beautiful girls, now being mourned by the finest families in Kiev.

All of them, thus transformed, swam sadly from right to left, from left to right, up and down, without stopping.

And now the sorcerer had just thrown a new goldfish into the fish pond.

There was a knock on the door. The mastiffs who guarded the accursed castle began to yap furiously; the elves who acted as Chernomor's servants rushed toward him, frightened out of their wits. There was a soft knock on the door of the accursed castle.

And a gentle, grave voice said: "Open, for pity's sake, to let in a lady traveler who has gone astray and is dying of hunger and fatigue!"

Chernomor ordered that the door be opened and saw before him a young girl of exquisite beauty. She was clad in cloth of gold; her *kokoshnik* was embroidered with pearls. She was tall, and as supple as a reed.

Chernomor was dazzled. "Who are you, beautiful lady, and why are you wandering like this over deserted roads, alone in this mysterious forest? I see by your attire that you are a great lady—a princess, perhaps? How does it happen that you are alone and without an escort?"

"While coming through this forest, I stopped to pick some flowers, became separated from my companions and could not find them again... I beg of you, noble lord, let me rest awhile, then let me be taken back to the home of my uncle, the grand duke of Kiev."

"Young lady, young lady, the castle is enchanted; once in it, one can never leave!"

The young girl essayed a sob, a sob that really sounded very natural.

"But do not lose hope" the sorcerer went on. "Your existence here may possibly be very happy and very enviable. Observe this splendid castle, come and visit the park, and look at this fish pond with many marvelous fishes. The most beautiful flowers, the most delicious food, the finest materials and the most precious jewels—all

51

of these can possibly belong to you."

"Truly!" exclaimed the girl, struck with wonder. "And what must I do to possess all these treasures?"

"To have them all, you need only consent to marry me."

"Oh, I am only too willing! But let me fish for one of these handsome fish that I desire so greatly, fish for him with the pretty silver net that you are wearing in your belt!"

The sorcerer smiled at the whimsical request and handed her the net.

Ruslan, the wise and valiant knight, threw the net, calling out: "This is the fish that I want!" And as soon as the sorcerer was caught in its web, he became a frightful toad that Ruslan crushed underfoot with his heel.

And marvelous to see, their enchantment ended, all the most beautiful daughters of the noblest families of Kiev, among them the Princess Olga, who smiled tenderly at her savior, came out of the water.

"Tsar Ivan sends greetings and blessings to his people and announces to them that the marriage of his daughter, Princess Olga, to the knight Ruslan will be celebrated in the near future. Throughout the kingdom there will be great rejoicing, and the celebration will last for several weeks!"

The glass mountain

Once upon a time there was a great king whose daughter died suddenly, and all of the inhabitants of the country were grief-stricken, for the princess was beautiful, gracious and beloved. But it happened that, on the day when she was to be buried, there arrived from a far country a wise man, a magician, who, on seeing the signs of national mourning, wanted to know the cause. As soon as the reason was explained to him, he betook himself to the palace and declared:

"The princess is not dead; let her rest."

Then he approached the king and said to him:

"You should not put the princess in a grave. I will make a glass chest, where she will sleep until the day when she is destined to awaken."

The king, delighted, announced that he would give the stranger a magnificent reward if what he had prophesied came to pass. The wise man immediately went to work. In one of the rooms of the palace he had a large glass chest set up, and in it the princess was

53

stretched out on downy cushions. At the door to the room, sentries were assigned to keep watch day and night and were officially ordered to permit no-one to enter.

All of these basic arrangements having been made, the wise man said to the king:

"Send laborers out in every direction to collect large amounts of supplies, for I must construct an oven larger than your capital and make a glass mountain. In seven years, when the skylark's song rings out, heralding the beginning of summer, send messengers throughout the countryside to summon to your presence any suitors for your daughter's hand, and announce that she will be the bride of him who can ascend the glass mountain, either afoot or on horse-back. In seven years and seven days, the princess will awaken and will give a gold ring to him who has reached the glass summit, and you will give her in marriage to that man, even if he is the poorest of your subjects; otherwise she will go to sleep again, this time never-more to awaken."

The king promised to follow all these instructions faithfully and immediately gave the order to collect the large quantity of supplies demanded by the magician. By the end of the sixth year, the oven rose up as high as the clouds. Two thousand workers were regularly employed in the task, and it was heated in such a way that ponds, rivers and lakes were dried up as a result, and exceptionally deep springs visibly diminished.

While this great enterprise was being completed, let us enter the cabin of a peasant, located a short distance from the city. An old man lived there with his three sons. The first two sons were vigorous and alert, but the youngest seemed slightly simple-minded. The old man, who had fallen ill, called them to his bedside and told them:

"I know that my end is approaching, and I would like to acquaint you with my last wishes. As for you, my elder sons, you must conti-nue to cultivate your fields together and to live in the same house, as long as you are not married, for a proverb says: "In a place where seven brothers can easily live together, there is not enough room for two wives." When the day of your weddings arrives, you will divide my inheritance between the two of you, and as long as he lives you will provide room and board for George, your young brother, who is in no condition to work or to run a household. It is on this condition that I bequeath you my money box. George is not very bright, but he has a good heart, and he will obey you as he has always obeyed me."

The two older brothers answered their father with smooth and eloquent words. The youngest said nothing, but wept bitterly.

"One more word", the old man continued. "After I am buried, I should like you to give me a last show of affection by coming, one after the other, to spend a night on my grave."

The two older sons once again agreed to this request with fine-sounding words, but without a tear in their eyes. The youngest once more said nothing but wept bitterly.

Soon afterward the old man died. His two heirs invited their neighbors and their friends to his funeral, seated them at a table overflowing with delicacies, and ate and drank as if it were a wedding feast. George remained alone near the coffin, sighing and weeping, and when the coffin was lowered into the ground, it seemed to him that all joy was dead and buried with his father.

That evening, after the last guests had departed, he asked his brothers which one of them wanted to spend the first night by the paternal grave.

"Oh", they replied, "this day has been very tiring; we really need to rest. You have done nothing; you can very well keep watch tonight."

Without any comment, George marched off to the cemetery and walked gingerly around the grave in which his father lay. At midnight, a voice he could not forget pronounced these words:

"Who is walking so softly toward my coffin?"

And he answered:

"Oh, dear Father, it is me, George, your youngest child."

The voice then asked why this nocturnal visit had not been made by one of his older sons.

George replied that the funeral activities had tired his brothers.

"All right", said the father. "Each favor rendered deserves to be rewarded, and I will give you your reward. One day, you will want to have fine clothes so that you can appear in the company of distinguished persons. At that time, return to my grave, strike the ground three times with your left heel and say: "Dear Father, I demand my reward for my first vigil." Immediately you will have a suit of armor and a horse. But not a word of all this to your brothers."

At the break of day, George returned home and went to sleep.

That evening, he asked his brothers which of them wanted to spend the night by the paternal tomb, and they answered him in a sarcastic tone:

"No one is going to snatch our father from his grave. If it pleases you to go to spend the night near him, nothing prevents you. But with all your vigils, you will not bring him back to life."

George listened sorrowfully to these words and returned to the cemetery.

At midnight, the voice of his father repeated the question:

"Who is walking so softly toward my coffin?"

And George replied:

"Oh, dear Father, it is me, George, your youngest child."

The father asked once more if one of the two older brothers had not come. George excused them by saying that they were exhausted by the day's work.

"All right", answered the voice of the dead man. "Each favor rendered deserves a reward. I will give you yours.

"The day will come when you will need a garment still finer than the one you earned yesterday. At that time, return here, strike my tomb three times with your left heel, and say: "Dear Father, I demand my reward for my second vigil." You will then receive such a beautiful suit of armor and such a handsome horse that you will never weary of looking at them. But not a word of all this to your brothers."

At the break of day, George returned home. His brothers were still in bed. He lay down on the stove and fell asleep.

That evening, he asked which of them wanted to spend the night at the grave site. They answered him in a sarcastic tone:

"He who voluntarily has spent two nights there can very well spend a third. Besides, what purpose does it serve? No one is going to kidnap our father, and he is not going to get out of his grave by himself. When he made his odd request, he was no longer in his right mind."

On hearing them talk like that, George burst into tears and returned to the cemetery. At midnight, the voice of the dead man asked:

"Who is walking so softly toward my coffin?"

And the dutiful son replied:

"Oh, dear Father, it is me, George, your youngest child."

"Why did your brothers not come?"

"They were exhausted by the day's work."

"All right. Each favor deserves to be rewarded. I will give you your reward. The day will come when you will realize that the more a man possesses, the more he wants. The wishes of the loving son who has been loyal to his father's memory must in justice be granted. I had wanted your brothers to share my wealth; now you alone will inherit. If the clothing and the horses that you earned yesterday and the day before yesterday are not enough, return here, strike my tomb three times with your left heel and say: "Dear Father, I demand my reward for the third vigil." You will then receive the finest suit of armor and the most magnificent horse imaginable. Everyone will admire you, your brothers will envy you, and you will become the son-in-law of a powerful king. But not a word of all this to your brothers."

At the break of day, George returned home and went to sleep. While he was sleeping, his brothers asked themselves:

Of what use to us is this fellow who roams abroad at night and sleeps during the day? Why should we feed him? With what he eats we could fatten a pig; that would be more profitable...

"Let him go away far from here!" exclaimed the older of the two. "Let him beg for his bread!"

"No", responded the other. "People know that we are financially solvent, and we would be criticized if we forced him to beg for handouts. Let him stay here. We will give him our leftovers, not enough to satisfy his appetite, but enough to keep him from starving to death."

While this was going on, the enterprise ordered by the magician was brought to a conclusion, and the king had an announcement made throughout the land that the hand of his daughter would be given to the man who, afoot or on horseback, ascended the glass mountain. At the summit of this mountain the princess lay sleeping in her glass chest.

From every side there came into the capital a multitude of individuals, some of them resolved to attempt the difficult feat, the others eager to witness the strange competition. In the distance, the mountain shone bright as the sun.

The peasant's two older sons had had elegant suits made for themselves so they could be a part of the great assemblage. George, to whom they gave only an old and ugly garment to wear, was told to stay in the house so they would not be humiliated by his miserable appearance. But as soon as he had watched them leave, he ran to the cemetery, struck the earth with his heel and said: "Dear Father, I demand the reward for my first vigil." Instantly there appeared before him a handsome horse, completely saddled and caparisoned. On his flanks hung a bronze suit of mail that fitted the body of the young orphan so well that it seemed made to order for him.

Hundreds and hundreds of would-be suitors had already tried unsuccessfully to scale the mountain. They had barely been able to take a few steps on the steep and slippery slope. George, wearing his suit of armor and with his face concealed beneath the visor of his helmet, rode through the center of the crowd and tranquilly scaled the mountain up to one third of its height. At that moment the princess could be seen to raise one hand as she lay in her glass chest. But he returned, saluted the king and disappeared.

That evening, he listened silently as his two brothers discussed the events of the day and the impressive performance of the knight in bronze armor.

The next morning, the two departed in haste to witness the contest, that was scheduled to last for two more days. As he had the day before, George went to invoke the aid of his father. Immediately there appeared before him a superb horse with a silver bridle, bearing a silver suit of armor.

As had happened on the preceding day, a number of contestants had striven in vain to reach the appointed goal. At high noon, George rode through the crowd and managed to ascend halfway up the mountain. At that moment the princess could be seen to move her head. But he turned around, saluted the king and disappeared.

That evening, sitting quietly in his abode, he listened to his brothers relate the events of the day and said nothing.

The next day, both of the brothers went back to the city, where there was an even greater crowd than there had been the day before. For it was a fateful day, the day of decision when, after sleeping for seven years, the princess was supposed to awaken.

In the morning George went off to the cemetery, struck the earth three times with his left heel and said: "Dear Father, I have come to claim the reward for my third vigil." Immediately he saw near him a horse with a golden bridle, bearing a splendid suit of armor also of gold, that fitted the young orphan to perfection.

At noon, he arrived in the midst of a legion of contestants who had failed in their efforts; he rode in the direction of the mountain and ascended it up to the very summit. Then the cover of the glass chest broke open, and the princess rose, took from her finger a gold ring and handed it to the glorious knight.

George descended the mountain slowly, saluted the king and disappeared.

The next day, the happy king announced that the hand of his daughter would be given to the man to whom she had presented the gold ring; and suddenly, coming through the crowd of courtiers and envious contestants and approaching the splendors of the palace, they perceived a young man dressed like a beggar. It was George. His two brothers gazed at him in stupefaction, and the king shuddered at the prospect of marrying his daughter to a creature of such a wretched mien. However, he could not fail to keep his word. George handed him the gold ring. George aspired to become his son-in-law and awaited the king's pronouncement. As soon as he heard it, he removed his hideous, shabby garment with one stroke of his hands and was revealed clothed in the brilliant armor in which he had ascended to the summit of the mountain.

The dutiful orphan was married to the sleeping beauty, and they lived happily ever after. The cruel brothers died, in the throes of envy and furious anger.

The triplets

Once upon a time there was a good honest peasant who was married to a good honest wife. Both of them got along well, happy to do good works, respected and much beloved by their neighbors, and seemed supremely happy. Yet they had one great sorrow, for which they could not be consoled by any strokes of good fortune. Wed for ten years, they were without children.

One evening when the good peasant had gone out, his wife, alone in their home, let her sad thoughts take over and wept, regretting that she was thus being deprived of the joys of maternity. Suddenly she felt at her feet a slight movement, like the playful caress of a young kitten. She looked down and saw a dwarf, one of those small magical creatures who inhabit gold and crystal caves in the mountains, and occasionally become attached to a human family and take pleasure in protecting and enriching it.

"Do not cry," he said to the good peasant woman. "Your wish will be granted. You will be a luckier mother than even you can imagine, and when my prophecy has been realized, I shall return."

61

With these words he disappeared; it was as if he had slipped out through the hole in the lock or through a crack in the floor.

Approximately one year later the good woman, who had hoped so fervently she might have the happiness of becoming a mother, presented the world in the course of several minutes three handsome, healthy and perfectly formed boys. As he had promised, the dwarf visited her anew and said:

"Your sons will make a substantial fortune and will be a great joy to you until the day of your death."

As he spoke, he climbed like a cat to the edge of the crib in which the triplets lay and, taking from his little pocket a ball of red wool, attached a strand to the feet of one of the boys, to the hands of the second and to the forehead of the third. Then he instructed the mother:

"The evening before the day when these infants are to be baptized, do not forget to remove and to burn this thread. You will gather up the ashes with a spoon and, after mixing them with a few drops of milk, you will put the mixture on the body of each of your boys. My work will then be completed, and each of them will have extraordinary powers in the part of the body where I have knotted this thread. Farewell! You will not see me again."

The three boys grew rapidly, and simultaneous with their development, each of them became distinguished by an unusual skill. Thanks to the magical gifts they had received, one of them became known as Keen Eye, the second as Skillful Hand, and the third as Light Foot. In the years of their early youth, with the complete agreement of their parents, they resolved to travel to a foreign country and to find there a profitable employment that would make use of their powers and skills. They left by three different roads, promising each other that at the end of three years, they would have a reunion in their parents' house.

Light Foot went in the direction of the Orient, and in a short time completed the long trip, for he was able to cross plains and mountains at great speed without growing tired. He entered the service of a king who owned a number of horses, several of whom were so wild and so wary that no one could stop them. But Light Foot could run even faster than the most agile of the steeds. In an instant he had tamed the rogue horses and brought them to join the herd. The task that fifty shepherds working together had been unable to accomplish, he had done easily all by himself.

The king, who was a just man, paid him the salary of fifty shepherds; in addition, he gave him many presents. One day, at a banquet to which he had invited a considerable number of lords and princes, he began enthusiastically to describe the skill with which his young shepherd controlled and herded his horses. One of his guests commented that the shepherd might not have any difficulty being in charge of animals who knew his voice, but that he would like to see him deal with the animals of another region.

He was put to the test. Unfamiliar horses, chosen because they were exceptionally fiery, were released on a huge plain. Not only did Light Foot follow them, but he outdistanced them as they advanced headlong. He was rewarded for this new exploit with the praises and presents of the lords and princes who at first had been skeptical about his astonishing powers. His name became famous throughout the regions of the Orient. Whenever a sovereign wanted a message delivered without delay, he entrusted it to Light Foot and paid him generously. All of those who employed him thus would have liked to retain him. But the day having come when he had to depart to rejoin his brothers, he set forth with twenty horses laden with the treasures he had accumulated.

The second brother, Skillful Hand, who had made his way to the south, found everywhere as much work to do as he was willing to accomplish. Without belonging to any organization, without having learned any trade, he succeeded in everything he undertoook. He was able to act successively, with equally good results, as a tailor, a cobbler, a carpenter, a goldsmith; in each case, in an instant the chore was performed perfectly.

One day he arrived in the capital, where everybody was in a state of great excitement. War had been declared. It was necessary to send troops against a powerful enemy as soon as possible, and they had not enough arms, uniforms and boots for these troops. All of the laborers were toiling day and night without letup. But there were not enough of them, and they had too many things to do.

In order to finish the job, some workshop heads were asking for five months, others for six months, others for still longer. Skillful Hand guaranteed the king that he could complete everything in three months.

"And what guarantee," asked the king, "can you give me to persuade me to trust you?"

"I have neither gold nor silver," replied Skillful Hand, "but my life is in your hands. And tomorrow morning, if the king agrees, I will show him a sample of my work."

The next day, true to his word, he exhibited a garment that he had just sewn, and the tailors, after examining it very carefully, could not find in it even the slightest defect.

Skillful Hand then took over all the tasks that had been divided among a good number of workshops. It was thought that he would summon all of the workers in the city to help him, and pay them huge salaries. But they were wrong. He set to work all by himself, conscious of the talents he possessed, and two months before the stipulated deadline he had finished his chores, and done them admirably and completely. The king, delighted, showered him with gifts and wanted him to accompany the king to battle, declaring that someone who could perform such miracles with a workingman's tools must be equally gifted with a sword. But although he thanked him, Skillful Hand responded that he had to return home to his parents, to whom, thanks to his achievements, he would be able to offer a substantial sum of money.

The third son, Keen Eye, who had directed his steps toward the regions of the west, wandered for a long time before he found suitable employment. Because of his skill as a hunter, he found it easy to provide for his daily needs, but not to become rich. One day he arrived in a city whose sovereign was in a state of great distress because of a strange adversity. This king had in his garden a marvelous tree that bore golden apples, very large and quite valuable. These apples were counted regularly, and sentries guarded them around the clock. In spite of this surveillance, in three nights three of the apples had been stolen; no one had seen the thief, nor had anyone found any clue to his identity.

After listening to the recital, Keen Eye said: "Provided that this robber is not altogether immaterial, I assure you that I will see

Сидить Козакъ въ конъ грає що ...
... жить тоже має

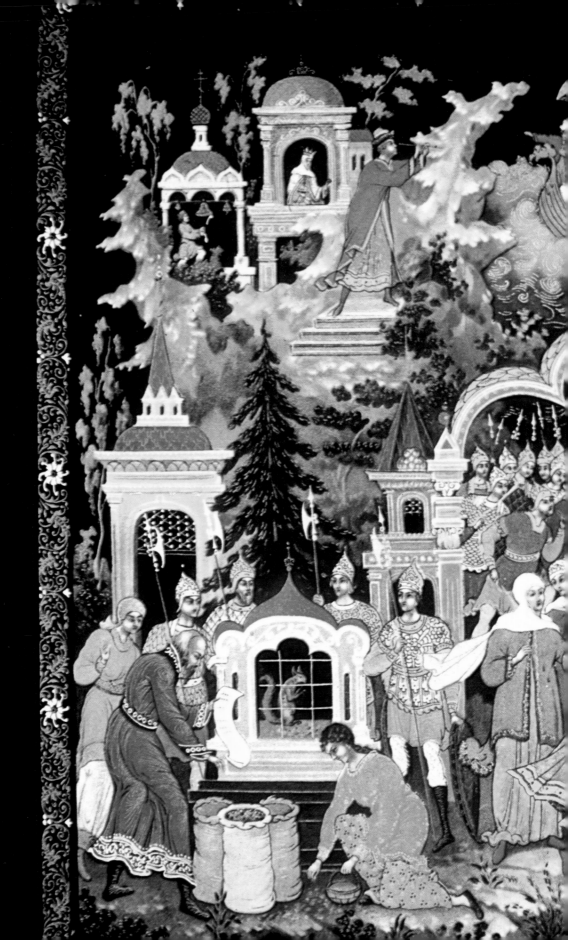

him." And having discussed the matter with the king, he climbed to the top of a tree, from which he could see without being seen, without the knowledge of the sentries in the garden. At the same time, the guards formed such a tight cordon around the apple tree that not even a mouse could have penetrated it. Keen Eye kept watch for the whole day without observing any move by the criminal. In the evening, at sunset, a small yellow butterfly fluttered around the apple tree, then alit on a branch where one of the golden globes shone. Certainly such a frail insect was not going to be able to remove one of the heavy apples. The last ray of sunlight disappeared over the horizon. The shadows of night spread over the earth. But lanterns were lit around the precious tree, and there was still not the least sign of any attempt at theft.

About midnight, Keen Eye, who had been seated on his branch since morning, dozed. A few minutes later he awoke and looked around. The butterfly had disappeared and, with him, the golden apple near which he had settled had also vanished. The king was furious when he learned of this new act of larceny and wanted the guards, whom he accused of being delinquent in their duties, to be severely punished. Keen Eye did not dare to reveal his suspicions, realizing that they would believe him mad if he said that he believed the butterfly had made off with the golden apple. But he explored the city in search of a man familiar with the practices of sorcery, and when he discovered one, he asked him if he could not fashion a net that appeared to be very light but was nevertheless solid enough to withstand heavy pressure.

"Yes," replied the magician, "it is possible." He took three spiders, cast a spell over them that gave them extraordinary powers, enclosed them in a box and said to Keen Eye:

"Carry these spiders wherever you wish, show them the place where you want them to operate, and they will manufacture a web that Mana himself, Mana the supreme sorcerer, would be unable to break."

As he had the previous evening, Keen Eye went to his post in the garden. As had happened the day before, he saw the yellow butterfly alight. Then, with the aid of a ladder, he gently transported his magic box to the tree whose fruit he was determined to protect from any onslaught. The three spiders immediately set to work and soon had captured the greedy insect in their web.

At midnight, a loud noise could suddenly be heard. Where the butterfly had been, there appeared a little man with a gray beard who was holding an apple in his hand and struggling in the net, trying in vain to tear it apart. At the cries uttered by the guards, who were trying to seize the thief, the king came running.

"There," said Keen Eye, "our man has been captured just as I hoped. Now we can go to sleep, and tomorrow morning we can question him."

The next day the sorcerer of the day before, Keen Eye and the guards accompanied the king to where their captive was still struggling in the net.

"Who are you?" the sorcerer asked him.

"You don't want to answer? We'll see about that."

"Who are you?" he repeated, putting a burning ember under his chin.

"Take away that flame," exclaimed the little man, moaning, "and I will answer your questions."

"Who are you?"

"I am the servant of the sorcerer Pirisilla."

The sorcerer burned his beard with the ember.

"Stop!" he implored. "I will tell you the truth. I am the son of Pirisilla."

Finally, after the question had been posed a third time, he confessed:

"I am Pirisilla himself."

Then the sorcerer, the burning ember in his hand, commanded him to reveal the place where he had hidden the golden apples. And once they had all been recovered, the evil sorcerer who used his powers only to perform bad acts was burned up in his web.

The king, ecstatic at having regained possession of his treasured belongings, gave Keen Eye some superb presents, and would gladly have retained him in his service. But the young traveler felt he had to return to the paternal abode.

In their adventurous travels, the three brothers had accumulated a fortune with which they would henceforth be able to lead a life of luxury in their native land. But one day they heard about a king in the north who had promised to give his daughter in marriage to the man who could accomplish three extremely difficult feats, that none of her suitors had yet been able to perform; and they decided once again to test their force and their skill by accepting this challenge.

When they arrived near the capital, which had attracted a number of lords desirous of wedding the beautiful princess, Light Foot went ahead of his brothers to find out what the three difficult feats were. He learned that in the morning one had to lead to pasture a wild reindeer, endowed with such strength that in a few hours he could circle the whole earth, keep watch on him all day, and bring him back in the evening. Then one had to close the door to the castle; in the lock of this door was an enchantress who, with a force not to be resisted, seized by the hand the daring person who might attempt to draw the bolt, squeezed him unmercifully, roughly swung him above the wall, and finally let him fall to earth, half dead. The third feat was no easier than the first two: a man was standing on the top of a mountain, holding an apple between his teeth by its stem; without wounding him, the contestant had to hit the apple with an arrow and cleave it in half.

Each of the three brothers, thanks to his special gift, could undoubtedly do one of these three things. But the rule was that all three should be done by the same man. To accomplish their purpose, the ingenious triplets had recourse to a ruse. They had identical features and figures, so that it was almost impossible to distinguish one from the other. They cut their hair and their beards in the same style and had made a magnificent garment, with which each could adorn himself in succession. The three exploits having been performed, since only one would be entitled to receive the reward, fate would decide which one of them would have the good fortune of marrying the princess.

Everything was arranged accordingly. Keen Eye and Skillful Hand remained hidden at some distance from the city, while Light Foot, wearing the garment embroidered in gold and strewn with diamonds, presented himself to the king as a rich foreign lord and asked to undertake the first test.

"Tomorrow if you wish," said the king. "But I advise you to wear a different, less expensive garment, for the reindeer will drag you through bramble bushes and marshes."

The young suitor replied: "What does the price of my garment matter?"

The princess observed him through the hole in the lock and hoped that he might succeed.

The next day, at sunrise, Light Foot put a stout rope around the neck of the reindeer and held onto the end of it. As soon as the door of the stable was opened, the unruly animal rushed outside and ran with the swiftness of the wind, while all of the spectators admired the ease with which the young stranger followed him. But when the reindeer had gone beyond the houses and was on a deserted plain, Light Foot, realizing that no one could see him and not wanting to tire himself unnecessarily, leaped on the animal's back and thus enjoyed a peaceful ride. The reindeer, understanding that this time he had met his master, stopped his headlong course and began to graze. About noon, he lay down on the ground and fell asleep. Light Foot slept alongside him, and in the evening brought him back to the stable. Such a thing had never been done before. Light Foot was admired, feted, and had the honor of dining at the king's table. Then he retired, saying that he was going to rest, but actually in order to rejoin his brothers and relate to them the events of the day.

The next day Skillful Hand put on the rich garment and went to the city to submit to the second test. The king, mistaking him for the swift runner of the day before, renewed his congratulations and informed him of the danger to which he was exposing himself by trying to close the enchanted door later that day. The princess, who peered at him through the hole in the lock and also believed that he was the knight she had already seen, hoped that he might succeed.

The shrewd lad betook himself to a blacksmith and had an iron hand made. That evening, when everyone in the castle was asleep, he heated this hand in the fire. Then he ascended a ladder to reach the bolt that he was to draw. When the sorceress tried to seize him, he held out the burning iron hand. She drew back, uttering a sharp cry of pain, and he easily achieved his goal. The next day the king, seeing that the famous door was closed, enthusiastically congratulated the young suitor on this new success and invited him to dinner. Afterward Skillful Hand asked permission to retire in order to rest, he explained, from the ardors of the task performed during the night and to prepare himself for the last ordeal.

Leaving the palace, he went secretly to rejoin his brothers. The next day Keen Eye donned the rich costume and presented himself to the king as the happy victor of the two previous days. Seeing him, the princess said to herself:

"If he can only succeed in his undertaking this one more time, I shall be glad to marry him."

At the top of the mountain was the man holding an apple in his teeth by its stem. Keen Eye advanced through the crowd of curious bystanders, glanced at the target, placed such a long distance away that it could barely be perceived, adjusted his bow, and let his arrow fly. Lo and behold, the apple was cut in two. The spectators vigorously applauded this marvelous display of skill. The eyes of the princess were wet with tears of joy, and the exuberant king was ready to celebrate the engagement immediately. But Keen Eye was mindful of his contractual agreement. He begged the king kindly to postpone the happy event until the following day and went to rejoin his brothers.

According to the conditions laid down at the beginning of the adventure, the luck of the draw had to determine which one of them would claim credit, not only for his own victory, but also for those of the two others. It was Keen Eye who won the royal wedding in the drawing. Light Foot and Skillful Hand congratulated him with a sincere joy in his good fortune, embraced him affectionately and departed for their own country, having had their fill of adventure and desiring only to live in peace with their fortune, close to their parents.

Keen Eye married the princess, ascended to the throne after the death of his father-in-law, and ruled the realm wisely.

Let the fire burn,
you cannot put it out

In a village there was once a peasant named Ivan Stcherbakov. He lived a happy life. He was still in his prime, and he was considered the best worker in the country. In addition, he had three sons who helped him. One was married and another engaged; the third, still an adolescent, was beginning to plow the earth.

Ivan's wife was capable and a good housekeeper, and his daughter-in-law was as gentle as she was hard-working. Ivan could have lived very happily with all of his family. There was not a single useless mouth in the house except for the old, ill father (he was asthmatic and for the past six or seven years had sat near the stove without budging).

In Ivan's abode, ease and comfort reigned. He possessed three horses and a foal, a cow and her calf, and fifteen sheep. The women themselves made the socks and the clothing of the peasants and worked in the fields, and the peasants performed their assigned tasks. The bin contained more bread than would be needed before the next batch came from the oven. There were enough oats to pay all the taxes and provide for all the needs of the household.

Therefore Ivan had only to live peacefully with his children.

Unfortunately, he had a neighbor, Gavrilo, a cripple, the son of Gordéï Ivanov, and a feud developed between them.

During the lifetime of old Gordéï, when Ivan's father was master of the house, the peasants lived on good terms with one another. If the women needed a broom or a bucket, the men a tool or a spare tire, they went from one *izba* to the other to procure it; like good neighbors, they exchanged favors. If a young calf ran into the threshing room, they limited themselves to chasing him away, saying: "Don't let him come in here, for our sheaves are not yet stacked." It never occurred to them to hide him or shut him up in the room, in the shed, or to vilify one another.

This was the situation when the senior generation was in control. But when the younger people took over the management of the household, the relations changed.

The cause of it all was a mere bagatelle.

The hen of Ivan's daughter-in-law began to lay her eggs early; the young woman kept the eggs for Holy Week. Every day she found one egg beneath the shed, in a wagon bin. But once the hen, probably frightened by some children, jumped over the hedge into the neighbor's yard and laid there. The young wife heard the hen cackle and thought: "I haven't the time right now, I have to clean the *izba* for the party. Later I'll go and pick up the egg."

That evening she looked beneath the shed; in the wagon bin, no egg. She asked her mother-in-law and her brother-in-law if they had taken it.

"No," they said, "we did not take it."

Taraska, the younger brother, told her:

"Your hen laid in your neighbor's barnyard; she was cackling there, and she came back from there."

The young woman went to her neighbor's. The old lady came to meet her.

"What do you want, my daughter?"

"Well, Grandmother, my hen flew over to your property today; did she not lay an egg there?"

"We didn't see anything. We picked up our eggs; we have nothing to do with anyone else's. I assure you, my daughter, that we do not go into our neighbor's yard to collect eggs."

The young woman, insulted by these words, responded angrily, her neighbor went her one better, and they ended by squabbling. Ivan's wife, coming back from drawing water, joined in the argument. Then Gavrilo's wife also came out and began to reproach her neighbor in no uncertain terms, mixing truth and fiction. The quarrel grew more bitter. All of them talked at the same time, trying to outshout one another, and the more words, the more accusations...

"You are a this... You are a that... You are a thief... You are a tart... As for the old man, your father-in-law, you let him starve and leave him stark naked!"

"It's you who are a thief... You took my sieve and you sold it. You kept my yoke; give it back to me."

They seized the yoke, they spilled the water, fichus were grabbed off, and hair pulled out.

Gavrilo, who was coming back from the fields, came to the defense of his wife. Seeing this, Ivan ran over with his son and joined the fray. Ivan was a sturdy fellow. He knocked everyone about and pulled out a fistful of Gavrilo's beard.

Some men intervened, but it was only with great difficulty that they separated the combatants.

This was the origin of the falling-out.

Gavrilo collected the hairs of his beard, wrapped them in paper and went off to the village courthouse to seek redress.

"I didn't let my beard grow," he said, "so that that Ivan with his ugly mug could pull it out."

His wife informed anyone who would listen that Ivan was going to be convicted and sent to Siberia.

And their hatred grew by leaps and bounds.

From the beginning the old man had urged reconciliation, but the young ones would not listen to him. He told them:

"My children, you are behaving very foolishly. Reflect for a moment: all this excitement about an egg! The children picked up an egg? Much good may it do them! There is nothing of great value in an egg... God has made enough of them for everybody... And then the old lady said a bad word? Teach her to improve, to speak more politely... You fought? Who doesn't do that at times? Go on, make up and let that be the end of it. If you stubbornly persist in hurting one another, you are the ones who will suffer."

But the young people refused to listen to the oldster. What he said they did not perceive as wisdom, but as senile ramblings.

Ivan would not make peace.

"I didn't pull out his beard," he said. "He himself tore it out, hair by hair, while his son ripped my shirt all up. Look."

They appeared before the justice of the peace and the judge of the village.

While the trial was going on, the linchpin of his cart disappeared from Gavrilo's house. The women accused Ivan's son of committing the theft.

"During the night, we saw him pass in front of the window and approach the cart," they said, "and a village gossip reported that he went to the saloonkeeper and offered him the linchpin."

They returned to court, and every day there were disputes and battles between one household and the other.

The children repeated the insults of their parents, and when the women happened to be together at the river, their tongues flapped more energetically than their laundry paddles, and it was always to call one another names.

At the beginning the two peasants confined themselves to slandering one another, but gradually they extended their argumentative exchanges to anything that happened to be handy. What was more, they encouraged their wives and children to follow their example. Everything went from bad to worse.

Ivan Stcherbakov and Gavrilo sought redress from the *mir*, from the judge of the village and the justice of the peace. Soon they had worn out all of the judges. Sometimes it was Gavrilo who tried to have Ivan ordered to pay a fine; sometimes Ivan bestirred himself attempting to have Gavrilo locked up in the station house. And the more they attacked one another, the greater their hatred. When two dogs come to grips, the longer they fight, the more furious they become; if one of the two is struck from behind, he thinks the other one has bitten him and is more enraged than ever. Thus did the two peasants react. They went to court, each in turn was punished by being fined or imprisoned, and each time this occurred, their irritation with one another grew. "Just wait, and you'll pay for this!"

For six years this situation remained the same.

Only the old man, lying on the stove, was forever harping on the same thing, hoping to make them listen to reason.

"What are you doing, children? So forget all your differences; you are not acting in your own interests. Therefore don't persist in putting down your neighbor; that will only stir him up more. The more stubborn you are, the more you will suffer as a result."

But no one would listen to the old man.

During the seventh year, one day, at a wedding, Ivan's daughter-in-law began to abuse Gavrilo in front of the whole gathering, crying out that he had been encountered with some horses that did not belong to him.

Gavrilo, who had been drinking, lost control of himself and struck the woman. He struck her so hard that she had to take to her bed for a week, and she was pregnant at the time.

Ivan, delighted at the opportunity, went to register a complaint with the examining magistrate. "At last," he thought, "I shall be rid of my neighbor; he will certainly be sentenced to a jail term and perhaps even exiled to Siberia."

But he was promptly disappointed. The magistrate did not honor his request; they had visited and examined the woman, who was on her feet and bore no trace of any blows.

At that Ivan hastened to the justice of the peace, who sent him to the village court. There, he behaved so shrewdly, giving the secretary and the president a *half-bucket* of sweet brandy, that he managed to have Gavrilo sentenced to be whipped.

The decision was read to Gavrilo. The secretary read: "The court orders that the peasant Gavrilo Gordéï be punished by being given twenty lashes on his back, in the presence of the court officer."

Ivan also listened. He looked at Gavrilo. What would he do now? Gavrilo cocked an ear. After he had heard the reading of the order, he became as white as a sheet, turned around and went out into the hall. Ivan followed him. As he was heading toward his horses, he heard Gavrilo saying: "Very well, you are going to flog my back, and my back will burn, but take care that you are not burned by something even worse!"

Ivan immediately went back to see the judge.

"Your Honor," he said, "he is threatening arson. Listen to what he said in front of witnesses."

Gavrilo was summoned.

"Is it true that you said that?"

"I said nothing. Flog me, since you have sentenced me to suffer that. I understand clearly that I alone must be punished for telling the truth, while he is permitted to do anything at all."

Gavrilo wanted to say still more, but his lips and his cheeks began to tremble, and he turned toward the wall. The judge himself was frightened when he looked at the man. "I trust he is not contemplating an act of violence against himself or against his neighbor!" he thought.

And the elderly judge said to both of the men:

"Come on, my friends, and be reconcilied; that is the best course... You, Gavrilo, are you not ashamed of having struck a pregnant woman? Happily, the good Lord protected her; otherwise, your conscience would be heavy in the aftermath of a grave sin. Is that good? Tell me, is that good? Admit before him that you have been at fault, be repentant, and he will pardon you; and we shall reverse our sentence."

But the secretary intervened:

"It is impossible," he said, "for a friendly reconciliation, provided for in Article 117, has not taken place; a judgment has now been made, and such judgment must be executed."

The judge would not listen to him.

"Enough talk," he said. "The first article, brother, is as follows: above all, one must obey God, and God has ordered the reconciliation."

And once more he attempted to make the peasants see reason.

A waste of breath: Gavrilo remained intractable.

"In one year I shall be half a century old," he said. "I have a married son, and I have never been struck by anyone, and now today this human devil of an Ivan has had me sentenced to be flogged, and it is I who am going to ask him to pardon me!... No, no, enough. Ivan will have reason to remember me."

Again his voice trembled, he was unable to go on speaking, and he turned and left the room.

From the court to their homes, the distance was ten *versts;* it was late when Ivan returned home. The women had already gone to bring back the cattle. He unhitched his horse and entered the *izba:* no one. His sons had not yet returned from the fields; the women were still with the cattle.

Ivan sat down on a bench and began to reflect. He recalled how pale Gavrilo had been when the decree was read and how he had turned away toward the wall. He put himself in the other man's place: suppose it had been he, Ivan, who had been sentenced to be flogged! And he felt pity for Gavrilo.

All of a sudden he heard the old man coughing and moving around; then he let his legs hang over the stove and got down. The oldster descended and dragged himself to the bench where Ivan was seated. The effort tired him; he coughed again, then put his elbows on the table and asked:

"What about it? was a sentence imposed?"

"He was sentenced to suffer twenty lashes," Ivan answered.

The oldster shook his head.

"What you are doing is bad," he said. "Oh, it is very bad! You are not doing harm to him, but to yourself. So they are going to beat his back. Will you feel any better as a result, I ask you."

"He won't do the same thing again!" replied Ivan.

"What won't he do again? In what respect did he act any more outrageously than you?"

Ivan grew choleric.

"What! What did he do?" he said. "Why, he just failed to kill a woman, and at present he is threatening to set fire to my property. In addition, you want me to ask him to pardon me?"

The oldster sighed and said:

"Ivan, you can travel throughout the world, while I, for some years now, have had to remain squatting on the stove, and because of that you imagine that you know everything and I know nothing... No, little one, you understand nothing. Anger blinds you. The sins of others you see in front of you, but your own lie hidden behind your back. What did you say? He did you harm?... But if he were the only one to behave badly, there would be no harm done. Is harm ever accomplished by a single person? No, it is always the product of at least two individuals. You perceive his misdeeds and do not see your own. If he alone were wicked and you good, there would be no harm done. Who, then, pulled out the hairs of his beard? Who spoiled the haystack? Who has been pursuing him from court to court? You accuse him of all sorts of things, yet you yourself are not behaving any better than he; that is where the harm comes in. My son, that is not the way I have lived, and it is not the way I have taught you to be.

"Did we live thus, we oldsters, his father and I? How did we live? Like good neighbors. Were we without flour? His wife came over. 'Uncle Frol, I need some flour.' 'My daughter, look underneath the shed and take as much as you need.' He had no one to take care of his horses. 'Go along, Ivan, and be responsible for his horses.' If I needed something, I went to his house. 'Uncle Gordéï, I need this or that.' 'Take it, Uncle Frol.'

"That is how we dealt with one another, and everything went swimmingly... But today, what is happening between you? Once upon a time, a soldier spoke to us about Plewna; is your war not worse than the war of Plewna? What sort of a life do you lead? What a sin!... You are the master, the head of the family; you are responsible for everything. And what are you teaching your wives and children? To live like dogs. Yesterday Taraska, the little whippersnapper, said the most awful things to his Aunt Anna, and his mother just laughed... It that something to be proud of? is it pretty? You will be the first to be hurt by it. Think a little about your soul... You insult me, and I respond by insulting you twice; is that the way a man should act? No, my dear fellow. Our Lord, when he walked the earth, did not teach us that, us poor fools. If someone addresses you with a bad word, don't answer him, and he will be ashamed of himself. This is what the Lord taught us: If someone smite you on one cheek, turn to him the other cheek, say, "Strike me if I deserve it,' and he will be ashamed; he will regret his act and place himself at your side. This is what He has commanded us to do, not to be proud... Well! Why are you silent? Is it not the truth?"

Ivan listened and was mute. The old man was afflicted by such a violent coughing spell that he had great difficulty recovering. Finally he continued:

"Do you think that Jesus Christ came among us to teach us to do wrong? No, it was always to help us, for our good... Look at what your life is like. Do you feel better or worse since this Plewna has come between you? Figure out how much you have laid out for the expenses of the judicial proceedings, for travel, for food. You have sons, truly young eagles; you would only have to live tranquilly, increasing your assets, whereas they are decreasing. Why? Always because of your pride. You should be able to go to the fields with your children and sow wheat, and here you are, obliged to run to a judge or a business agent. You do not plow, you do not sow at the proper time; she gives nothing for nothing, our good Mother Earth. Why was the oat crop unsatisfactory? When did you sow it? Only on your return from the village. And what did you gain? One more worry to shoulder. Ah, little one, be concerned only with your business affairs. Dig in the earth with your children, and stay at home. If someone injures you, forgive him. Thus you will have adequate time to attend to your chores, and you will be aware that your heart is lighter."

Ivan still said nothing.

"Here is what I have to say to you, Ivan. Listen to the words of an old man. Please go and harness your horse, return to the court by the same route as before, withdraw all of your complaints and then, tomorrow morning, go to Gavrilo's house, and invite him to visit you. As it happens, tomorrow is a feast day (it was the eve of the Nativity); prepare your samovar and buy some brandy. Forget all of these wrongs once and for all, and let them not be discussed further. Give this order to your wife and children."

Ivan sighed and thought: "What the oldster says is true."

He was no longer angry, but he did not know how to set about making peace.

As if he had guessed the thoughts of his son, the oldster continued:

"Go on, Ivan, don't hesitate, put out the fire at the start; once it is lit, you will no longer be able to control it."

The old man had still more to say, but he could not continue, for

the women entered the *izba* and began to chatter like magpies. They already knew that Gavrilo had been sentenced to be flogged and that he had threatened them with arson. While in the fields, they had even found the time to quarrel with the women in Gavrilo's family.

They reported that Gavrilo's daughter-in-law had threatened them, saying there was a member of the court who was supposedly protecting Gavrilo. He was now going to change the thrust of the trial; as a first step, the schoolmaster was drawing up a new petition against Ivan to be given to the tsar in person. In this petition no detail would be omitted: not the linchpin, or a certain vegetable patch, or anything else. Half of Ivan's assets would be turned over to Gavrilo.

Ivan listened to them, and his heart was chilled anew. He no longer desired to make peace with Gavrilo.

In the life of a peasant, there is always some chore to attend to. Without delaying in order to chat with the women, he rose, left the *izba* and went into the area under the shed. While he was performing his work there, the sun had time to set, and the boys also had returned from the fields, where the two of them had tilled the earth so they could sow the winter wheat.

Ivan went to meet them, questioned them about their accomplishments and helped them arrange everything. In order to repair it, he put aside a torn harness; he even wanted to bring the poles inside, but it was beginning to grow dark. So he left the poles, fed the animals, and allowed Taraska, who was leaving for the night with his horses, to depart.

"There's nothing left to do but to eat supper and go to bed," Ivan thought. He took the torn harness and headed toward the *izba*. He was no longer thinking about Gavrilo or about what his father had said to him. He had already taken hold of the chain and was entering the vestibule when he heard his neighbor, behind the hedge, denouncing someone in a hoarse voice. "The devil!" Gavrilo shouted. "He deserves to be killed!"

At these words, the old anger at his neighbor was rekindled in Ivan's heart. He stopped and lent an ear. Gavrilo had stopped talking. Ivan entered the *izba*. The fire was already lit; the young woman, in a corner, was at her spinning wheel; the old lady was preparing the meal; the oldest son was braiding *laptis;* the second held a book in his hand, and Taraska was getting ready to leave for the night. Everything would have been very peaceful in the *izba* had it not been for his anger at his neighbor.

Ivan was in a bad humor. He chased the cat off the bench and scolded the women because the bucket was not in its proper place. Discontented and grumpy, he sat down and started to repair the harness. He could not get out of his head Gavrilo's pronouncements, his threats in court, and also the words that he had uttered just a little while before in a hoarse voice: "He deserves to be killed!"

The old woman prepared supper for Taraska, who ate, put on his little coat and his caftan, girded himself, took a piece of bread and went outside toward the horses. His older brother wanted to accompany him, but Ivan himself rose and walked to the stoop.

The darkness outside was now total. Clouds covered the sky, and the wind began to blow. Ivan came down from the stoop, helped his son mount one of the horses, drove off the colts, stopped, looked and listened. Taraska was withdrawing into the distance, galloped into the street, joined some other boys, and they all left the village.

While Ivan was thus staying near the porte-cochere for several minutes, he could not help remembering the words of Gavrilo: "Take care that you are not burned by something worse."

"He is a man who will not retreat," thought Ivan... "It is very dry in this moment, and now the wind is taking a hand. He can secretly worm his way somewhere, set a fire in the back, and afterwards, what use looking?... He will set a blaze, the rogue, and he will be right again... Oh, if I could catch him in the act, he wouldn't get out of it so easily!"

This idea took root in his head so deeply that instead of ascending the stoop again, he passed through the porte-cochere, reached the street and rounded the corner of the house. "I shall go back there to my courtyard. Who knows? I should not overlook anything."

Ivan began to skirt the wall, taking regular steps. After turning the corner, he looked along the length of the hedge, and it seemed to him that something had moved at the other corner, something that had risen up abruptly from behind the wall.

Ivan stopped and held his breath. He listened and looked; every-

thing was quiet. The wind alone stirred the little leaves of the wil-
lows and whistled in the thatches. It was so black that he could
not use his eyes, but eventually they became accustomed to the
obscurity, and Ivan could distinguish the corner, and the plow that
was there, and the eaves of the *izba*. He remained thus for several
moments, looked and saw no one. "I may not have seen too well,"
Ivan said to himself, "so in spite of everything I will make a tour
of the area."

And he advanced, groping and feeling his way, skirting the outside of the shed.

In his *laptis* he walked noiselessly; he could barely hear his own
footsteps. He reached the corner and looked around. Suddenly,
at the other end, he saw something glitter near the plow, then
disappear.

The effect was that of a dagger in his heart. He stopped. In the
same place something glittered anew, with a brighter radiance,
and he distinctly saw a crouching man, his back turned, in a cap,
who was lighting a clump of straw.

Ivan's heart fluttered in his chest like a bird. He summoned up
all of his strength and started to run toward the man with great
strides. He did not even feel the ground under his feet. "Well,
well," he thought, "I have caught you red-handed."

He had taken barely a few steps when a great fire blazed up, but
not at the place where the sparks had glittered; no longer was it
a faint glimmer, either, for the straw of the eaves was aflame, and
the flames were falling on the roof.

Gavrilo was standing there, where he could be seen plainly. Like
a kite who swoops down on a skylark, Ivan hurled himself at the
cripple. "I am going to tie him up," he said to himself; "he will not
get away."

But the cripple, undoubtedly hearing his footsteps, turned around
and—how could he display such agility?—began to hop along the
length of the shed like a rabbit.

"You shall not escape!" called Ivan, rushing in hot pursuit.

He was going to seize him by the collar when Gavrilo slipped out
of his hands and grasped him by the trousers of his suit. The
trousers tore, and Ivan fell. He arose quickly and began to call out:

83

"Help! Help! Stop him!"

And he continued his pursuit.

While he was getting up, Gavrilo had arrived almost at his court-yard. But Ivan overtook and was about to grab him when suddenly something stunned him, as if a stone had struck him in the head. It had been Gavrilo who, near his house, had picked an an oak beam and, at the instant his adversary was hurling himself at him, had vigorously directed a telling blow to his head.

The blow stupefied him, he saw thirty-six stars, his eyes were veiled over, and he reeled. When he regained full consciousness, Gavrilo was no longer there. It was as bright as if it were high noon and, in the direction of his courtyard, something sputtered and flashed like a machine.

Ivan turned around. The back of his shed was all aflame, and the front was already beginning to burn, and amidst dense smoke, flakes of fire and burning straws were falling on the *izba*.

"But what does that signify, my friends?" cried Ivan.

He raised his hands and let them fall back on his thighs. "I had only to remove the clump of hay on the eaves and to stamp on it," he thought.

"What then is happening, my brothers?" he repeated.

He wanted to cry out, but he lacked breath; he could not utter a single word. He wanted to run, but his legs, seemingly stuck to one another, refused to obey him. He dragged himself along slowly, took a few steps, reeled, and again found it difficult to breathe. He halted, got his breath back and once more advanced on foot. Before he was able to turn to the back of the shed and approach the site of the blaze, the side of the shed caught fire in turn. A corner of the house was also burning, as well as the porte-cochere, and flames shot up from the *izba*. It was no longer possible to enter the court-yard.

A great crowd came running, but there was nothing they could do. The neighbors carried out their furniture and led forth the cattle.

From Ivan's courtyard, the fire spread to Gavrilo's. The wind had risen, and the flames were pushed across the street. Half of the village was destroyed.

They could rescue only the old man from Ivan's *izba*. The rest of the family saved themselves as best they could. Except for the horses, that had been put out for the night, they had to abandon everything. The cattle were burned alive; the chickens were set ablaze in their chicken coops; the wagons, the carts, the plows, the harrows, the chests of the women, the wheat under the sheds, every-thing was completely demolished. On Gavrilo's property, they managed to save the cattle and part of his possessions.

The fire continued to burn throughout the night. Ivan remained near his courtyard, looking and reduced to repeating:

"What then is happening, brothers? One could merely have taken the burning straw and put it out."

When the roof of his *izba* collapsed, he strode into the very heart of the fire, seized a blazing beam and attempted to remove it. The women noticed him and called to him loudly. But he withdrew his beam and went back to get another. He reeled and fell into the fire. His sons rushed to his aid and drew him from the flames. Ivan's beard, hair and clothing were burned, his hands lacerated, but he was not even aware of it.

"Grief has made him mad," they said in the crowd.

The intensity of the fire started to diminish; Ivan, however, was still in the same place, ceaselessly repeating:

"But, brothers, what is happening? One only had to take out the straw."

Toward morning, the ancient of the village sent his son to look for Ivan.

"Uncle Ivan, your father is dying, and he is asking for you."

Ivan had forgotten his father; he did not understood what was being said to him.

"What father? Who is asking for me?" he responded.

"He is asking for you. He is dying in our *izba*. Come, Uncle Ivan," said the ancient's son, pulling him by the hand.

Ivan followed him.

While they were removing the old man, some blazing straw had fallen on him, and he had been severely burned. They had taken him to the ancient of the village, who lived in a fairly distant section that the conflagration had spared.

When Ivan arrived to see his father, he found in the *izba* only the old wife of the village leader, together with some children seated on the stove. All of the others had run off to the fire. The old man was stretched out on a bench, a candle in his hand, his eyes turned toward the door. When his son entered, he stirred slightly. The old woman approached and informed him that his son was there. He asked him to draw nearer. Ivan approached, and the old man said to him:

"Well, Ivan, what did I tell you? So who set fire to the village?"

"It was him, Father!" replied Ivan. "It was him; I caught him in the act. With my own eyes I saw him set the roof on fire... I had only to seize the burning straw and stamp it out underfoot, and nothing would have happened."

"Ivan," said the old man, "I am going to die, and you too will die. Who has sinned?"

Ivan looked at his father and was silent. He was unable to utter a single word.

"Tell me, in God's name: who has sinned? What did I tell you?"

Then only did Ivan regain full consciousness. He understood. His nostrils flared, he fell to his knees, burst into tears and said:

"Father, it is I who have sinned. Forgive me! I am guilty before you and before God."

The old man gestured with his hands. He took the candle in his left hand, lifted the right hand to Ivan's forehead and tried to bless him, but was unable to complete the act.

"God be praised! God be praised!" he said, once more gazing at his son. "Ivan! Oh, Ivan!"

"What, Father?"

"What shall we do now?"

"I do not know, Father, how we are going to live from now on."

The old man closed his eyes and moved his lips, as if to call on the last remnants of his strength, then opened his eyes again and murmured:

"You will live... You will live with God."

The old man stopped talking, then smiled and went on:

"Listen, Ivan, do not denounce the arsonist. If you conceal the sin of another, God will forgive two of yours."

And the old man, taking the candle in his two hands, clasped them over his heart, heaved a sigh, stiffened and died.

Ivan did not denounce Gavrilo, and no one knew what had caused the fire. And in his heart Ivan no longer harbored any bitterness toward Gavrilo. The latter was amazed that Ivan failed to denounce him. First he was afraid; then he was reassured. The peasants did not quarrel any more, nor did their families. While they rebuilt their houses, the two groups worked side by side in the same courtyard. When the village had been reconstructed and the courtyards located farther apart, Ivan and Gavrilo once more became neighbors, and both of them lived in peace and harmony, as their fathers had before them.

Ivan Stcherbakov constantly recalled the last words of the old man and the teaching of God: that a fire must be extinguished as soon as it starts. And if someone does a man harm, he should not resort to vengeance but try to arrange things; and if someone uses insulting and offensive words, he should not respond by using worse ones. On the contrary, he should wonder how he could make the other understand that one should not speak hotly and teach the same lesson to the women and children in his family.

And Ivan Stcherbakov realized it was a good idea to follow these precepts and lived more happily and better than he had before.

Story of
Ivan the Imbecile

In the Kingdom of a certain country there lived a rich peasant. He had three sons: Simon the Warrior, Tarass the Pot-Bellied, Ivan the Imbecile, and a mute daughter, Melanie. Simon the Warrior went off to serve the tsar; Tarass the Pot-Bellied left for the city, to work for a shopkeeper; and Ivan the Imbecile, along with the daughter, remained at home, working and increasing their savings.

Simon the Warrior, as a reward for his services, received a promotion to a higher rank and property, and married the daughter of a lord. He had an impressive salary and a vast amount of land, but he felt he still did not have enough.

What the husband collected, the wife spent, and they were always without money.

One day when Simon paid a visit to his holdings to request some funds, his manager told him: "There is nothing to withdraw. We have neither cattle nor tools, neither horses nor cows, neither plow nor harrow; we must buy all these, and then money will be coming in." And Simon the Warrior went to his father's home.

"My father, you are rich," he said, "and you have given me nothing. Give me the third of your estate that is due me. I will use it to improve my land."

The old man answered:

"You have contributed nothing to the household; why should I give you a third? That would be unfair to Ivan and the girl."

Simon insisted:

"He is an imbecile and she is a mute. What do they need?"

The old man replied:

"All right. It shall be as Ivan wishes."

And Ivan said:

"Agreed! Let him have his share."

Simon the Warrior gained possession of his patrimony, used it on his estate, and returned to the service of the tsar.

Tarass the Pot-Bellied also earned a great deal of money. He married the daughter of a shopkeeper. But he was constantly embarrassed financially. He went to see his father and said:

"Give me my share."

However, his father did not want to give him, either, the share he was demanding.

"You have brought us nothing," he told him. "Everything we have in the house has been paid for by Ivan. I can't endanger his interests, and those of the girl as well."

Whereupon Tarass asked:

"What does he need, that imbecile? He won't ever be able to get married; no one will want him as a husband. And a mute girl does not need anything, either... Ivan," he added, "give me half of the wheat; I won't ask for any of the swing-plows, and of all your stock I want only the gray horse. You don't use him in the field."

Ivan began to laugh and said:

"Agreed! I will give him to you."

So Tarass too received his share. He transported the wheat to the city and led the gray stallion away. And Ivan, who had nothing left except for an old mare, plowed the earth and nourished his father and mother.

The old devil was very upset that the three brothers had made these arrangements without acrimony and were on good terms when they left one another. So he summoned three little imps.

"Listen," he said to them. "There are three brothers: Simon the Warrior, Tarass the Pot-Bellied and Ivan the Imbecile. Instead of quarreling with one another, they live in perfect harmony. It is the Imbecile who has thrown a monkey wrench in my plans. Go, take all three of them in hand and make them so angry at one another that they'll tear each other's eyes out... Are you capable of doing that?"

"We are," they said.

"And how will you do it?"

"This is how. We will begin by ruining them so that they don't even have enough to eat; then we will reunite them, and they will be at each other's throats."

"That's fine," said the devil. "I see that you know your business. Go, and don't come back until you have embroiled all three of them; otherwise, I shall punish you cruelly."

The imps went into their swamp to settle on their course of action. They discussed it and discussed it; each one wanted to assign himself the easiest task. Finally they decided to draw lots to determine what each would do; if one of the three finished his assignment before the others, he would then assist his two companions. The imps drew lots, and agreed on the day when they would meet again in the swamp to find out who had finished his chore and whom he would have to help.

When that day arrived, the imps reassembled in their swamp. They began to speak about their project. The first reported on Simon the Warrior.

"My efforts have been fruitful," he said. "Tomorrow, Simon will go to his father."

His companions asked him how he had managed this.

"My first task," he said, "was to instill in Simon such courage that he promised the tsar that he would conquer the whole world for him. So the tsar made Simon the commander-in-chief of the Army and sent him to make war against the Indian tsar. The armies were already facing each other. That same night, I dampened the powder in Simon's camp; then I went to the base of the Indian tsar and manufactured out of straw a countless number of soldiers. When Simon's men observed that soldiers, made of straw, were advancing on all sides, they were afraid. Simon then ordered them to fire, but neither the cannons nor the guns would go off. Simon's soldiers, terrified, fled like sheep. And the Indian tsar cut them to shreds. Simon was roundly denounced. His land has been commandeered, and they want to execute him tomorrow. Only one day's work remains for me to do: remove him from prison so that he can return home. By tomorrow everything will be finished. Therefore let me know which of you two I should be ready to assist."

The second imp reported on Tarass.

"My assignment is also going very well; I do not need any help. Within a week Tarass will see a change in his position. First I began by swelling his belly and increasing his avarice. He has become so greedy that he wants to acquire everything he sees others possessing. He has bought a great many things with his money, and now be is buying still more, but with borrowed funds. He carries a heavy load on his shoulders, and he is caught so tightly in the net that he will be unable to escape. In a week his payments will be due; I have transformed his merchandise into manure; he will not be able to pay and will go to his father."

They asked the third imp how things were going with Ivan.

"What can I say?" he answered. "Things are going badly. I started out by spitting in the crock of *kvass* to give Ivan a stomach-ache. I went over his property and I hardened the soil so that he would not be able to till it; that is, I thought he would be unable to till it, but the Imbecile came with his plow and undertook to dig up the soil. He had a very hard time, but continued nevertheless. Then I broke his plow. He returned to the house, picked up another and started to plow once more. So I went underneath the earth to seize the plowshare, but I was not able to hold onto it. He was continuing to push the plow, and the plowshare was sharp; it bloodied my hands. He has tilled amost the whole area; only a single strip is still to be done. Please help me, my brothers, for if we don't get the upper hand over him, all our efforts will be for naught. If the Imbecile continues to work, he will not be miserable, and he will feed his two brothers."

The imp of Simon the Warrior promised to come to his aid the next day, and they separated.

Ivan had tilled his whole field except for one strip. He had come to finish his work. He had a stomach-ache; however, he still needed to plow. He detached the earth from the plowshare, turned the plow upside down and made his way to plow another furrow. But he had barely begun this new furrow when he felt he was being stopped as if by a root. It was the little imp who was clinging to the plowshare and holding it back. "How strange," thought Ivan. "For there was no root there before, and now there is one!"

He thrust his hand into the furrow and, while groping, encountered something soft. He seized the object and pulled it out. It was black like a root, and something was moving on the root. "Ah, a living imp! Here, dirty creature!"

And Ivan made a gesture of breaking his head against the ground, but the imp started to whine:

"Don't strike me, and I will do whatever you wish."

"And what will you do for me?"

"You have only to say; anything that will please you."

Ivan scratched his head.

"My belly hurts. Can you cure me?"

"Yes," he said.

"Well, then cure me."

The imp bent over the furrow, dug, dug with his claws, withdrew a three-pointed root and held it out to Ivan.

"Here," he said. "You need swallow only a single one of these points to make your illness disappear."

Ivan tore off one of the three points and swallowed it, and his stomach immediately felt better.

The imp renewed his pleas.

"Now let me alone," he said. "I am going to bury myself under the ground and will no longer walk on the earth."

"Good! Go with God!" said Ivan.

As soon as Ivan pronounced this name, the imp sank into the earth like a stone to the bottom of the sea.

There remained only a hole.

Ivan concealed the other two points of the root in his cap and once more set about plowing the field. He finished the strip, turned over the plow and went to his lodging. He unharnessed, entered the *izba* and saw his older brother, Simon the Warrior, seated at the supper table with his wife. His property had been confiscated, and with great difficulty he had escaped from prison and taken refuge in his brother's home.

As soon as Simon saw Ivan, he said to him:

"I have come to live with you. Will you feed me and my wife until I find another refuge?"

"Certainly," said Ivan. "Live here in peace."

As Ivan went to sit down on a bench, the lady reacted with annoyance to his stench. She said to her husband:

"I cannot eat supper with a peasant who stinks."

Simon the Warrior turned toward Ivan.

"My wife says that you smell bad; you would oblige us by eating in the hall."

"Agreed," he said. "As a matter of fact, night has just fallen, and I must feed the mare."

Ivan took some bread and his caftan and left for the night watch.

Since the imp of Simon the Warrior was now free, he did as he had agreed to do with Ivan's imp and came to help him contend with the Imbecile. He made his way to the field and searched and searched for his companion: there was no one anywhere. He found only a hole. "My word," he thought, "evidently something unfortunate has happened to my companion. I am going to replace him. The earth is all plowed. I must ensnare the Imbecile during the hay-making."

The imp busied himself in the meadow and covered it entirely with a coating of mud. Toward dawn, Ivan returned from his night watch, took a scythe and went to mow the meadow. He reached it, tried to mow, swung once, then a second time; the scythe stopped and did not cut. He sharpened it. But in spite of all his efforts, Ivan was not accomplishing his chore. He said to himself: "I am going to return to the house. There, I will pick up a whetstone, and I will bring back some bread. If necessary, I will devote a week to the task, but I shall not go back until I have completed the mowing."

The imp heard him and thought: "He is stubborn, this Imbecile. I won't easily achieve my purpose. I have to find something else."

Ivan sharpened his scythe and again started mowing. The imp, creeping through the grass, grasped the end of the scythe in order to thrust it into the ground. Ivan had to work very hard, but nevertheless he somehow managed to finish his mowing. All that was left to mow was a small parcel of land by the swamp. The imp plunged into the swamp, saying: "Even if he cuts off all my fingers, this time I am not going to let him succeed!" Ivan headed for the swamp. The grass there was sparse, and yet he could not handle his scythe properly. He became angry and threw the scythe as hard as he could. The imp had barely time to avoid being hit.

Things were definitely going badly.

He hid under a bush.

Ivan, hurling the scythe again, sent it as far as the shrub and cut off half of the imp's tail. His finished his mowing, ordered the girl to gather the hay and went for his part to cut the rye.

When he arrived, he found the stems of the rye all entangled. The imp had passed by there. Ivan returned to his house, took a sickle to replace the useless scythe, and began to cut. He cut all the rye thus. "Now I have to get ready for the oats," he said.

The imp with the mutilated tail heard him and thought: "I didn't succeed in catching him in the rye, but I'll catch him in the oats. I'll do that little thing tomorrow morning."

At dawn, he arrived at the oat field. The oats were already cut. Ivan had worked during the night so as to lose less grain. The imp complained: "He has finished everything, and he has hurt me very much, has the Imbecile. Even during the war I have never had so much trouble. He doesn't sleep, the accursed fellow. Impossible to steal a march on him. Now I'll go to the stacks to make them rotten." And the imp sped to the stacks of rye, slipped into the sheaves and busied himself making them rotten. He heated them, warmed himself and fell asleep.

Ivan harnessed his mare and went off with the girl to gather the sheaves. He reached the stack, lifted two sheaves with the pitchfork and, presto, impaled the imp. He drew out the pitchfork, and what did he see? A living imp at the end of his pitchfork, and one with a severed tail! He wriggled, fidgeted, and tried to free himself.

"So, dirty creature, here you are again."

"I am another one," he answered. "The first one was my brother; at the time I was occupied with your brother Simon."

"It doesn't matter which one you are. You will suffer the same fate."

He wanted to crush him into the ground, but the imp begged:

"Let me go. I won't start in again, and I will do anything that you wish."

"And what can you do?"

"I can make soldiers from anything at all!"

"But what good is that?"

"You can do whatever you want, for a soldier is good for anything."

"Will they be able to sing?"

"Yes."

"Then make some."

"Take this sheaf of rye," said the imp, "shake the ears against the ground and say only: 'My slave orders you to cease being a sheaf, and let each of your ears be transformed into a soldier'."

Ivan took the sheaves, did and said as the imp had indicated; and the sheaf separated, and the stalks that constituted it became soldiers, with drums and bugles.

Ivan began to laugh.

"I find this truly amusing! It's really fun! It will delight the girls."

"Well," demanded the imp, "Aren't you now going to set me free?"

"No, I want to recreate the stalks; otherwise the grain will be lost. So teach me the method of changing them back to sheaves once again. I'll beat them with a flail."

"You have only to say: 'So many soldiers, so many stalks. My slave orders them to become sheaves once more'."

Ivan obeyed, and the soldiers were transformed anew into sheaves.

"Let me go now," the imp implored once more.

"Agreed!"

Ivan set him on the ground, held him with one hand, with the other liberated him from the pitchfork, and said: "With God!"

96

But as soon as he pronounced this name, the imp sank into the earth like a stone to the bottom of the sea.

There remained only a hole.

Ivan returned to the house. There he found his second brother, Tarass, and his wife, who were eating supper. Tarass the Pot-Bellied had been unable to pay his creditors and had taken refuge at his father's. He saw Ivan.

"Well, Ivan, while waiting for me to become rich again, will you feed me and my wife."

"Certainly," said Ivan. "Live here in peace."

Ivan removed his caftan and sat down at the table.

"I can't eat with the Imbecile," said the shopkeeper's wife. "He stinks of sweat."

Tarass the Pot-Bellied turned toward his brother.

"Ivan, you smell bad," he told him. "So go eat in the hall."

"Surely," replied Ivan.

He took some bread and went to the courtyard.

"Besides, it is time to go feed the horse and to leave for the night watch," he said.

Tarass' imp, having finished his task that night, went to rejoin his comrades as they had agreed, and to be in league with them against Ivan. He went to the field and searched and searched for his companions; there was no one. He found only a hole. So he walked to the meadow, found a tail in the swamp, and in the rye a second hole. "Oh," he thought, "they must have suffered some misfortune. Therefore I must replace them in order to oppose Ivan."

And the imp went off in search of Ivan. The latter, having already finished his work in the fields, was now in the act of felling trees in the woods. His brothers, who had decided they were somewhat too confined in Ivan's house, had ordered him to chop some wood and to build them a new house.

The imp ran to the forest, slipped into the branches and attempted to hamper Ivan in his work. Ivan hacked at the tree in a way guaranteed to make it fall on a spot that was empty, then pushed it; but the tree fell on the wrong side and became entangled with the nearby branches. Ivan took a pole to disentangle the tree, and had great difficulty forcing it to the ground. Then he attacked another tree and had the same experience. He toiled and toiled, and succeeded in felling it only after extraordinary exertions. He passed to a third tree; always the same situation.

Ivan had had the intention of cutting down about fifty young trees; he had felled even less than ten by the time night fell. He was irritated, steam escaped from him like a fog in a forest, and he still continued to work. He managed to feel one more tree, but his back was so painfully stiff that he could no longer endure the agony. He threw down his axe and sat down to rest.

The imp, seeing Ivan stop, was elated. "Good," he thought. "He is tired and is ceasing to work, so I too shall rest for a moment." Joyously he straddled a tree. But in the twinkling of an eye Ivan seized his axe, swung it and hurled it with all his force against the tree, that fell, split in two.

The devil did not have the time to pull back his legs; the branch broke and took one of his paws. Ivan set to work lopping off the branch.

He perceived a living imp. He was amazed.

"There you are, dirty creature! There you are again!"

"No," he said, "I am another one. I was with your brother Tarass."

"Whoever you are, you will suffer the same fate."

Ivan lifted his axe and was about to bring it down heavily on the imp.

But the latter implored him:

"Don't strike me, and I'll do for you anything that you wish."

"What can you do?"

"I can manufacture all the money you desire."

"Well, then, make some for me."

The imp said to him:

"Take some oak leaves, rub them in your hands, and gold will fall to the ground."

Ivan took some leaves, rubbed, and gold fell.

"It's a game to entertain children," he commented.

"So let me go,", said the imp.

"Agreed!"

Ivan took the pitchfork and freed the imp.

"Go with God!" he said.

But as soon as he pronounced that name, the devil sank into the ground like a stone to the bottom of the sea.

There remained only a hole.

The brothers had their house, and each one settled down in his dwelling. Ivan, having finished his work in the fields, brewed some beer and invited his brothers to come celebrate with him. But they refused.

"As if we didn't know what a peasants' party is like!" they said.

Ivan entertained all of the peasants and the women and drank himself. He even became a little light-headed and went into the street to look at the round singers. He approached them and asked the young girls to sing in his honor.

"I will give you something such as you have never seen in your life," he told them.

The women began to laugh and to sing his praises. When they had finished, they said to him:

"Well, give!"

"I am going to bring it to you right away." He took a sieve and went into the forest. The women laughed.

"What an imbecile!"

Then they completely forgot about him. But soon they saw him come running back, and the sieve held something.

"Well, do you want any?"

"Yes! Yes!"

Ivan seized a fistful of gold and threw it to the women.

"My ancestors!"

The women rushed forward to pick it up. The peasants also hastened thither and snatched at the gold pieces. An old woman was almost crushed underfoot. Ivan laughed.

"Oh, foolish people, why hurt an old woman? More slowly! I will give you still more."

And he once more began to toss gold by the fistful. Crowds gathered. Ivan had emptied the sieve. One demanded that he distribute still more. He said:

"No, that is all. I will give you more another time. Now let us dance and sing!"

The women started to sing.

"Your songs are not very pretty," he said.

"Do you know any better ones?"

"I will let you hear some in a very few minutes."

He went to the shed, took a sheaf, shook the ears against the ground and said: "My slave orders you to cease being a sheaf, and let each of your stalks be transformed into a soldier."

The sheaf opened up, and the stalks changed into soldiers. Drums were beaten and bugles blown. Ivan ordered the soldiers to sing and to parade in the street. The spectators were astonished. When the soldiers finished singing, Ivan led them back to the shed, expressly forbidding anyone to follow them, and once more changed the soldiers into sheaves. Then he returned home and went to bed.

In the morning, the older brother, Simon the Warrior, learned of all this and came looking for Ivan.

"Inform me," he said, "from where you took the soldiers and where you have hidden them."

"What do you want to do with them?"

"What! What do I want to do with them? Why, with soldiers you can do anything. You can conquer a whole kingdom."

"Oh, why didn't you tell me that sooner?" responded Ivan in astonishment. "I will make you as many of them as you want. As it happens, our sister and I have had an abundant harvest."

Ivan led his brother before the barn and said to him:

"Pay attention. I am going to manufacture some, and you will take them away, for if it were necessary to feed them, in one day they would eat the whole village out of house and home."

Simon the Warrior promised to see that the soldiers were led away, and Ivan knuckled down to his task. He shook a sheaf, and a company appeared; he shook another sheaf, and there was another. Eventually so many had come forth that the field was filled with them.

"Well, have enough men?" he asked.

Simon was satisfied. "Enough. Thank you, Ivan."

"I'm glad," he said. "And when you need more, I will make them for you. This year there is a great deal of straw."

Simon the Warrior gave his orders to the army, grouped them according to the rules and went off to make war. Hardly had he departed when Tarass the Pot-Bellied arrived. He also had just learned what had happened the day before. In his turn he asked his brother:

"Tell me where you find gold. If I could procure some for myself as easily as you do, with the gold I had I could accumulate all of the gold in the entire world."

"Really?" Ivan was stupefied. "Why didn't you tell me sooner? I am going to give you as much as you want."

His brother was overwhelmed.

"Give me at least three sieve-fuls."

"Surely," he said. "Let us go into the forest. First harness a horse; otherwise we will not be able to carry it all."

They left for the forest. Ivan rubbed the oak leaves between his hands and piled up a great heap of gold for him.

"Have you enough?"

Tarass was satisfied. "It is enough for the moment. Thank you, Ivan."

"I'm glad," he said. "When you need any more, come to see me, and I will rub some for you. There are a great many leaves."

Tarass the Pot-Bellied filled a whole wagon and went off to do business with it.

The two brothers had left: Simon to make war, Tarass to do business. Simon the Warrior conquered an entire kingdom; Tarass the Pot-Bellied accumulated a great deal of money. The two brothers met. Simon confessed to Tarass whence he had drawn his soldiers, and Tarass told him where he had obtained his money. And Simon the Warrior said to his brother:

"Now I have conquered a kingdom, and I live very well. Only I have not enough money to feed my soldiers."

And Tarass the Pot-Bellied said in turn:

"I have obtained a great deal of money, and my only concern is that I have no one to protect it."

"Let us go to our brother," Simon the Warrior proposed. "I will tell him to make some more soldiers, I will give them to you to protect your money, you will ask him to rub you some more money, and you will give it to me so I can feed my soldiers."

Both of them hastened to Ivan's house. When they arrived, Simon said to him:

"I have not enough soldiers, my brother; please make me some more, at least as many as can be manufactured from two sheaves."

Ivan shook his head in denial.

"I will not make them for you just like that, without a reason."

"Why not? You promised."

"That is true," he said, "but I will no longer make them."

"And exactly why, Imbecile, will you no longer make any more?"

"Because your soldiers killed a man. As I was plowing near the road, I saw a woman who was following a coffin and weeping. I asked her: "Who, pray, is dead?" She answered me: "It is my husband. Simon's soldiers killed him during the war." Here I thought that the soldiers were going to be singing songs, and instead I find that they have killed a man. So I shall not give you any more of them."

He persisted stubbornly and would make no more soldiers.

After that, Tarass the Pot-Bellied asked Ivan the Imbecile to make him some more gold.

Ivan shook his head.

"I will not make any more for you without good reason."

"What? You promised me!"

"That is true," he said. "Nevertheless, I will not make you any more."

"But tell me why, Imbecile, will you no longer make any more?"

"Because your gold pieces have taken Mikhailovna's cow away from him."

"Taken away, you say?"

"Yes, taken away! Mikhailovna had a cow, and his children drank milk. But one day recently the children came and asked me for milk. I questioned them: "Where, then, is your cow?" They replied: "The manager of Tarass the Pot-Bellied came and gave Mama three gold disks, and she gave him the cow. So now we no longer have anything to drink." Here I imagined that you were going to amuse yourself with those gold disks, and now I find you have taken milk from children. I will give you no more."

The imbecile persisted and would give him nothing. The two brothers left as empty-handed as they had arrived. As they walked along, they discussed possible ways to overcome their difficulties. Simon said:

"Listen; this is what we are going to do. You will give me money to feed my soldiers, and I will give you half of my kingdom and soldiers to guard your money."

Tarass accepted the offer. The brothers divided their assets, and now both of them were tsars and both were rich.

Ivan, who remained in the house, saw that his father and mother were nourished and worked in the fields with the mute girl.

One day Ivan's old watchdog fell ill and seemed to be dying. Ivan pitied him. He asked the mute for some bread, put it in his cap and went outside to throw it to the dog. But his cap had a hole in it, and a little root fell from it, along with the bread. The old dog swallowed it and the bread. And as soon as he had swallowed the root, he got up alertly, began to play and to bark and to wag his tail; he was completely cured.

The father and mother, who had witnessed what had occurred, were amazed.

"How did you cure the dog?" they asked.

"I had two little roots that could cure any illness. And it happens that the dog ate one of them," Ivan replied.

A short time after that, it came to pass that the daughter of the tsar became ill. And the tsar let it be known in all the cities and towns of his realm that he would give a magnificent reward to the person who could cure her and that, if that person were a bachelor, he would give him his daughter in marriage.

The news of this proclamation was received in Ivan's village.

Ivan's parents called him and said to him:

"Have you heard what the tsar has just announced? You tell us that you have a root; therefore go and cure the daughter of the tsar, and you will be happy for the rest of your days."

"A good idea," he agreed.

Ivan made ready to leave and got dressed. As he was going out, descending the stoop, he saw a beggar woman with a crippled arm.

"I have heard it said that you are a healer; heal my arm, for I cannot get dressed by myself."

"Certainly."

Ivan took out his root, gave it to the beggar woman and told her to swallow it. The beggar swallowed it and was healed. She was able to use her arm. Ivan's parents came out to say their goodbyes. But on learning that he had given away his last root and no longer had anything with which to cure the tsar's daughter, they showered reproaches on him.

"A beggar woman! You took pity on a beggar woman! And you feel no pity for the daughter of the tsar?"

Ivan did indeed pity the daughter of the tsar as well. He harnessed a horse, put some hay in the wagon and got up on the seat.

"But where do you intend to go, Imbecile?"

"To care for the daughter of the tsar."

"But you no longer have a cure."

"That does not matter," he said.

And he whipped his horse. He arrived at the court. He had barely mounted the stoop when the daughter of the tsar recovered. The tsar was ecstatic. He summoned Ivan, had him clothed in a rich costume and told him:

"You are going to become my son-in-law."

"So be it!" he said.

And Ivan married the daughter of the tsar.

The tsar died shortly afterward, and it was Ivan who succeeded him.

That is how all three of the brothers became tsars.

The three brothers lived and reigned.

The oldest, Simon the Warrior, lived a happy life. He had added many real soldiers to his straw soldiers. He ordered that, through-out his realm, one soldier be recruited for every ten houses, and that these soldiers be of tall stature, with white bodies and clean-cut visages. Thus he was provided with a large number, that he trained, and if ever someone refused to obey him, he dispatched soldiers and obtained what he wanted. Thus everyone feared him.

And his life flowed along happily. He realized all of his dreams; everything on which he laid his eyes belonged to him. He sent soldiers who appropriated for him everything that he desired and delivered it to him.

Tarass the Pot-Bellied also was happy. He had not wasted the money that Ivan had given him. On the contrary, he had seen that it bore fruit. He had put the affairs of his kingdom in order. He kept his gold in chests and demanded still more from his subjects. He demanded so much per village, so much per capita, so much on travel, so much on shoes and cloth strips, etc. And thus he had everything that he desired. In exchange for his money, everything he wished was brought to him, and people also came to work, for everyone always needs money.

Ivan the Imbecile was not too unhappy, either. As soon as his father-in-law had been buried, he removed his regal garments and gave them to his wife to enclose in a chest. He again donned his hempen shirt, his trousers, his shoes of bark, and once more became immersed in his work.

"I am bored," he said. "My paunch is starting to expand, and I no longer have a hearty appetite, nor do I sleep well."

He had his father, his mother and his mute sister summoned, and set to work.

He was told:

"But you are the tsar!"

"Oh, what does it matter? A tsar, too, needs to eat."

His minister came and told him:

"We have not enough money to meet the payroll."

"Very well," said Ivan, "if there's no money, don't pay the staff."

"But then they will all leave!"

"Very well, let them leave. They will then have time to work. Let them dispose of the manure: too much of it has accumulated."

His subjects came to Ivan to ask for justice. One complained that another had stolen his money from him.

"In that case, undoubtedly he needed it," said Ivan.

Thus everyone learned that Ivan was an imbecile.

His wife said to him:

"They say that you are an imbecile."

"All right, let them. Let them say it!"

Ivan's wife commenced to reflect; like him, she was an imbecile.

"What can I do?" she said. "I cannot oppose the will of my

husband. The thread must perforce follow the needle."

She took off her tsarina's robe, put it in the chest and headed toward the mute to learn how to work. She learned to work and volunteered to help her husband.

Soon all the sane citizens left Ivan's kingdom; only the imbeciles remained. No one had any money, everyone lived by working, fed himself and helped to feed others.

The old devil waited and waited for news of the imps, eager to find out how they had thwarted the three brothers. But after waiting a long time, he decided to set out to inform himself. He searched and searched; nothing anywhere, except for some holes. "Well," he thought, "they have not had the upper hand. It is necessary that I myself put my shoulder to the wheel."

He started off to look for the three brothers in their old lodgings, but they were no longer there; in fact; he found each of the three in a different kingdom.

All of the three were alive and ruling a realm.

The old devil was perturbed by this. "Well," he said to himself, "I myself will put my shoulder to the wheel."

First he paid a visit on Simon the Warrior. He went to see him not as himself, but in the form and aspect of a general.

"I have heard it said, Simon the Tsar, that you were a famous warrior," he declared. "I am an expert in depth on the science of arms, and I have come to serve you."

Simon the Tsar questioned him, found him to be intelligent and accepted his offer to serve.

The new general instructed the tsar in the art of organizing a strong army.

"The first requirement," he said, "is to have a large number of soldiers; otherwise, you would have in your kingdom too many persons who served no useful purpose. You should recruit all of the young people indiscriminately, so you will have five times as many soldiers as now. Then you must have the latest models in rifles and cannons. I will invent for you rifles that can shoot a hundred bullets at one time, bullets that will rain down like peas. And I will manufacture for you cannons that will shoot fire a great distance; whether it strikes a man, a horse or a wall, everything will go up in flames."

Simon the Tsar listened to the new general. He gave orders to draft all the young people and constructed new plants, where new rifles and cannons were manufactured. Soon afterward he went out to war against a neighboring tsar. When Simon was in the presence of the enemy, he ordered his soldiers to loose on them bullets from the rifles and fire from the cannons. In a single stroke he maimed and burned half of the opposing army.

The neighboring tsar was panic-stricken, yielded and ceded half of his kingdom to Simon. The latter was gratified. "Now," he said, "I am going to fight the Indian tsar."

But the Indian tsar knew of Simon's reputation. He imitated his inventions and even outdid him. Not only did he recruit all the young men, but also all the unmarried women in his kingdom, so that his army was even larger than that of Simon. He had the same kind of rifles and cannons and, in addition, he had found a way to fly in the air and to hurl explosive bombs from the sky.

When Simon the Tsar went to war against the Indian tsar, he expected to vanquish him as he had the other. But the scythe cut and cut and finished by stopping him. The Indian tsar did not allow the enemy to come within attacking distance. He sent women to fly above Simon's army and decimate it with explosive bombs. The women set about raining bombs on Simon's army, like insect powder on cockroaches. Simon's army took flight, leaving him all alone. The Indian tsar took possession of the kingdom of Simon the Warrior, while the latter fled wherever his feet led him.

Having thus finished with Simon, the old devil headed for the abode of Tarass the Pot-Bellied. He took the form of a merchant, settled in the kingdom and devoted himself to business. He paid generously for merchandise, and crowds rushed to his office in order to make money. They made so much that they were able to pay all of their back taxes, and the current taxes as well were paid regularly. Tarass the Tsar was elated. "I must thank this merchant," he thought. "For in the future I will have more money and be able to live better." Tarass the Tsar was tempted to engage in new enterprises; first, he wished to build a new palace for himself. He let his subjects know that they might bring him wood and stone and come to work for him. His monetary offer was a good one.

He expected that, in order to be paid by him, a crowd would rush to work for him, as they had formerly.

But this was not the case. He observed that the wood and stone were carried to the merchant, and that it was to the merchant that the workers directed their steps.

Tarass the Tsar raised his proposed payments. The merchant outbid him. Tarass had a great deal of money, but the merchant had much more. So he carried the day, and the palace of the tsar could not be built.

Tarass then had the notion that he'd like a garden planted. In the fall, the tsar announced to his subjects that they could come to work for him planting his garden. No one came. They were all too busy digging a pool for the merchant.

Winter came. Tarass the Tsar wanted to have a sable coat made for himself. He sent a man to purchase one. But the messenger returned and said:

"There is no more sable. All of the furs are at the merchant's; he has paid top price for them, and has had a carpet made for himself from the sables."

Tarass the Tsar needed to buy some trotters. He sent some men to buy them. The messengers returned and told him:

"All the trotters are at the merchant's; they are being used to transport water for his pool."

Thus Tarass the Tsar was unsuccessful in bringing any of his projects to fruition. His subjects were unwilling to do anything at all for him, while they did everything he wanted for the merchant; they brought him only the money the merchant had given them to pay his taxes. So the tsar had so much money that he did not know where to put it, but he was not living at all well. He had given up his projected enterprises, but it was becoming quite difficult for him to find the wherewithal to live comfortably. He lacked everything; all of his servants, his cooks and his coachmen had left him to go to the merchant, so that even food was starting to be in short supply. He sent to the market for something. Nothing could be found; the merchant had bought up all the stock. Only money for the taxes was delivered to him.

Tarass the Tsar became angry and had the merchant expelled

from his kingdom. The latter settled down just on the other side of the frontier and continued his operations. In exchange for his money, they brought everything to him, nothing to the tsar.

Everything was going from bad to worse for the tsar. He spent entire days without eating. And then the rumor spread that the merchant was boasting that he was buying the tsar himself.

Tarass the Tsar was afraid; he did not know what to do. Simon the Warrior came to his home.

"Help me," he said. "The Indian tsar has dispossessed me."

"What could I do?" replied Tarass. "I myself have not eaten for the last two days."

Having thus finished with the two brothers, the old devil made his way to Ivan's. In the form of a general, he wanted to persuade Ivan to organize an army in his kingdom.

"A tsar should not exist without an army," he said. "Allow me to act, and I will recruit soldiers from among your people and organize an army."

Ivan listened to him.

"All right," he said. "Do it, and teach them to sing pretty songs; that would please me."

The old devil left to make a tour of Ivan's kingdom, calling on volunteers to enlist. He announced that everyone would be welcome and that each recruit would receive a measure of brandy and a red cap.

The imbeciles could not help laughing.

"We have as much brandy as we want; we make it ourselves. As to caps, our wives make us caps of all colors, as well as multi-colored ones."

Subsequently, the old devil returned to Ivan's home.

"The imbeciles do not want to enlist voluntarily," he said. "I shall have to force them to sign up."

"Very well," said Ivan. "Then force them to enlist."

So the devil announced to the people that all the imbeciles should report to be drafted as soldiers, and that those who refused would be put to death by Ivan.

The imbeciles came to see the general.

"You say that if we refuse to enlist, the tsar will have us put to death; but you do not say what will become of us if we are soldiers. It appears that in that case we shall also be killed."

"Yes, that can happen."

On hearing this response, the imbeciles resisted more strongly than ever.

"We will not go," they said. "If we must be killed, we should prefer to die at home."

"You are really imbeciles! Imbeciles!" said the old devil. "It is possible that soldiers may be killed, but at least they have a chance to come out alive, whereas if you do not obey, Ivan will certainly have you executed."

The imbeciles thought it over, then headed for the home of Ivan the Imbecile.

"There is a general," they said, "who has ordered all of us to become soldiers. 'If you enlist,' he said, "there is a chance that you may not be killed, but if you do not enlist, the tsar, Ivan will certainly put you to death.'"

Ivan began to laugh.

"But how could I kill all of you all by myself?" he asked. "If I were not an imbecile, I would be able to explain this to you; as it is, I don't understand it myself."

"Then we shouldn't go?"

"Agreed," he said. "Do not go."

The imbeciles returned to the general and repeated their refusal to become soldiers.

The old devil perceived that things were not going well for him. He went to see the tsar of Tarakansk, whose confidence he had been able to win.

"Let us make war against Ivan the Tsar," he said. "The only thing he is lacking is money; he has wheat, cattle and all other assets in abundance."

The tsar, Tarakansk, went off to war. He assembled a large army, rifles and cannons, and marched to the border to invade Ivan's kingdom.

A messenger came to inform Ivan:

"The tsar of Tarakansk is going to war against you."

"Fine!" he said. "Let him."

The tsar of Tarakansk crossed the border with his whole army and sent his advance troops to reconnoiter the position of Ivan's army.

They searched and searched; no army. They waited to see if it might not appear over the horizon. There was absolutely no sign of it. Impossible to fight. The tsar of Tarakansk sent men to occupy the villages. The soldiers arrived in a village. The imbeciles, men and women, came out of their dwellings and gazed at the soldiers in amazement. The soldiers took possession of their wheat, their livestock. The imbeciles yielded up everything; no one tried to defend his property.

The soldiers occupied another village; the same thing occurred. Thus they marched for one day, then another; and everywhere the situation was the same. They were given everything, no one defended himself in protest, and the people of the region even invited the army to live with them.

"My dear friends," they said, "if living conditions are so bad in your country, come and settle with us permanently."

The soldiers marched and marched; still no army. Everywhere were people who lived peacefully, had enough to eat, did not defend themselves and invited the soldiers to come live with them.

Finally the soldiers began to be bored. They went to the tsar of Tarakansk and said to him:

"We have had no opportunity to fight. Command us to go elsewhere. If there were a war, fine and dandy! But here, we might as well be trying to walk on water. We certainly cannot make war here."

The tsar of Tarakansk grew angry. He ordered his soldiers to range over the whole realm, to ruin the villages, to raze the houses, to burn all the wheat and to kill all the livestock.

"If you do not obey," he said to them, "I will put you all to death!"

The soldiers, panic-stricken, carried out the orders of the tsar. They set to work burning the houses and the wheat and killing the livestock.

The imbeciles still did not defend themselves. They merely wept. The old men, the women, the children, all of them wept.

"Why are you harming us?" they asked. "Why destroy all of our possessions? If you need them, take them rather."

Finally this assignment sickened the soldiers. They refused to proceed any further, and the whole army broke up and scattered.

The old devil took his leave, understanding full well that he could not get the better of Ivan through using the soldiers. Soon he returned in the form of a wealthy gentleman, established residence in Ivan's kingdom and resolved to fight him by using money, as he had done in the case of Tarass the Pot-Bellied.

"I should like very much to make you prosperous," he said to them, "and to teach you a great many useful things. I intend to take a house in this vicinity and to establish an industry."

"Good!" they said to him. "Stay with us."

The next morning, the wealthy gentleman appeared in the public square with a great sack of gold and sheet of paper and said:

"You are all living like pigs. I should like to teach you how really to live. Construct a house for me, following these plans. You will work, I will superintend, and I shall pay you in gold."

And he showed them the gold. The imbeciles were impressed. They were not familiar with money; they bartered the products of their labors among themselves. They admired the gold.

"These pieces are pretty," they said.

And they went to work for the wealthy gentleman in exchange for the gold pieces. As he had done with Tarass, the old devil scattered gold by the fistful; in return, he received the fruit of their labor and all sorts of products.

Elated, he thought: "My affairs are in good order. I shall ruin the Imbecile just as I ruined Tarass, and actually buy him along with all of his imbeciles."

But when the imbeciles had collected enough gold pieces, they gave them to their wives to make necklaces for themselves; all the young girls put them in their hair, and the little children started to play in the street with them. The imbeciles decided that they had accumulated enough and did not want any more. However, the house of the wealthy gentleman was still only half finished, and he did not yet have enough wheat and livestock to last him for a year. He announced that workers could come and labor for him and bring him wheat and livestock, in exchange for which he would give them many gold pieces.

райская птица называемая р...

АЛКОНОСТЪ

птица ... ... алконосъ
близъ рая пребываетъ ...
... ... когда
глаз и теплы погудаетъ
тол сама себя ...

But on one came to work; no one brought him anything.

Only occasionally did a young boy or girl come to exchange an egg for a gold piece. That was all; he had nothing else to eat.

The wealthy gentleman was hungry. He made his way through the village, seeking to buy something to eat. He entered a courtyard and offered a gold piece for a chicken. The women refused the gold. "I have enough of them already," she said.

He left to call on another woman, who had no children, and offered her, too, a gold piece, this time for a herring.

"What would I do with it, with my payment?" she asked. "I have no children, no one to play with it. I have already taken three of these little gold objects as a curiosity."

From there, he went to visit a peasant to procure some bread. This man, too, refused a gold piece. "I don't need it," he said. "If you wish to be given something in the name of Christ, that is different. So wait; I am going to ask my wife to cut you a piece of bread."

The devil started to spit and ran away as fast as his legs could carry him.

He had been offered something in the name of Christ, and the mere mention of this name was to him more painful than the cut of a knife.

Thus he was unable to find any bread. Everywhere the old devil went, they refused to give him anything in exchange for his money, and they said to him: "Offer us something else, or work for us, or else: Take, for the love of Christ."

And the old devil had nothing to offer but money. He did not want to work, and to accept anything in the name of Christ was impossible.

The old devil became angry.

"What more do you want, since I am willing to give you money? With money you can buy what you want and hire as many people as you desire to work."

The imbeciles refused to listen to reason.

"No, no," they said, "it isn't worth the trouble. We don't have to pay anyone, and we have no taxes. So of what use is money?"

The old devil went to bed without dining. Ivan the Imbecile was informed about what was happening. Someone came to ask him:

"What should we do? There has appeared among us a respectable gentleman, who appreciates good food and is well dressed. He wishes neither to work nor to receive anything in the name of Christ. All he does is offer gold pieces to everyone. At the beginning, we gave him everything in order to obtain gold pieces, but now that we have enough of them, we no longer give him anything. What can we do for him so that he does not starve to death?"

"Well," answered Ivan, "he must have something to eat. Let him go from door to door like a beggar."

Thus the old devil was obliged to go begging from door to door. Finally he arrived at Ivan's house and asked the mute girl, who was preparing a meal for her father, for something to eat. The mute had so often been taken in by ne'er-do-wells who arrived just before dinner, without having worked, and ate all the gruel, that she had become an expert in recognizing them by their hands. Those who had calloused hands were invited to sit at table; for the others, there was nothing but scraps.

The old devil glided toward the table. The mute took his hand and examined it; no calluses, white hands with long nails. She began uttering hoarse sounds and pushed the devil back from the table.

Ivan's wife intervened.

"Do not be upset, worthy sir. My sister-in-law will not allow anyone who has not calloused hands to sit as a guest at our table. Wait awhile until we have finished dining, and you may have the leftovers."

The old devil was mortified to be asked to eat with the pigs in the house of the tsar.

And he said to Ivan:

"It is a stupid law, the law of your land that says that each person must work with his hands. It was stupid on your part to have enacted such a law. Does one work only with the hands? What do you think intelligent people work with?"

"How would we know, we who are imbeciles?" replied Ivan. "It is with our hands and our backs that we work."

"Because you are imbeciles. But I am going to teach you to work with your heads. Then you will see that that is preferable to physical work."

"What!" exclaimed Ivan, astonished. "Oh, it is not without reason, then, that we are called imbeciles."

"Only," said the old devil, "it is not easy to work with the head. You refuse to give me food to eat because I have not calloused hands, but you do not realize that it is a hundred times more difficult to work with the head. Sometimes it happens that the head splits."

For a time Ivan was thoughtful.

"Why then, friends, go to so much trouble? It is not good to have a splitting headache. In view of that, easy work done with the hands and the back is better."

"If I go to so much trouble," retorted the old devil, "it is just because I have pity on all of you imbeciles. Without me, you would remain imbeciles. But I, who work with my head, am going to teach you to follow my example."

Ivan was amazed. "Teach! Teach!" he said. "Our hands eventually get tired. So now we will be able to change; we will be able to work with our heads."

The devil promised to instruct them.

Then Ivan had published throughout his realm the fact that there had arrived a well-dressed gentleman who would teach them all to work with their heads, that one could perform tasks better by using the head than with the hands, and that each one of them should come to be instructed.

In Ivan's kingdom there was a very high tower, with a ladder standing upright the length of the wall and a platform at the top. Ivan had the fine gentleman ascend it, so that everyone could see him. The gentleman positioned himself up above them and started to speak. The imbeciles looked at him. They were convinced that the gentleman was really going to show them how to work without using the hands, with the head alone, whereas the old devil was actually utilizing words to teach them how to live without working.

The imbeciles did not understand him at all. They started for a long time; then each one returned to his chores. The old devil remained on the tower for a whole day, then another, speaking without stopping. But eventually he became hungry. It had never occurred to the imbeciles to send him up some bread. They thought that, working better with his head than with his hands, he would find it child's play to make some bread.

Still another day passed; the old devil, atop the tower, did not

115

cease discoursing. And the people approached him, one after the other, looked and looked, then went away.

"Tell me," asked Ivan, "has the gentleman begun to work with his head?"

"Not yet," they told him. "He is still prattling."

For one more day the old devil remained on the summit of the tower. He was becoming weaker. Once his legs buckled, and he hit his head against a pillar. An imbecile noticed this and reported it to Ivan's wife. The latter ran to find her husband, who was working in the field.

"Come look," she said. "They tell me that the gentleman has started to work with his head."

Ivan was astonished. "Really!" he said.

He turned his horse around and approached the tower. The old devil, completely exhausted, was reeling on his legs and knocking his head against the pillar. Just as Ivan arrived, the devil tottered, fell on the ladder and tumbled down, hitting his head against each rung one after the other.

"Oh, oh!" said Ivan. "So he spoke the truth, the fine gentleman. It is possible to split one's head! It is not like calluses; doing this kind of work, one risks receiving lumps on one's head."

The old devil fell, and his head sank into the ground. Ivan wanted to approach to see if he had accomplished a great deal of work, but suddenly the ground opened up and the old devil disappeared into the bowels of the earth.

There remained only a hole.

Ivan scratched his head.

"Oh, the dirty creature!" he said. "It is him again. He must be the father of the others; how large he is!"

Ivan is still alive. People are hastening en masse to settle in his kingdom.

His brothers have come to live with him, and he feeds them. To whoever comes to his house and says: "Feed us!" he answers: "Agreed. Take what you will; we lack nothing."

But there exists in his kingdom a law, one single law: he who has calluses on his hands sits at the table; he who has no calluses eats scraps.

Where love is, God is

There was once in a certain city a cobbler named Martin Avdieitch. He occupied a basement room into which light came from a single window, that overlooked the street. Through the window he watched people pass. It is true that he could distinguishh only their feet, but Martin Avdieitch recognized the passers-by by their boots. He had lived for a long time in the same place and was acquainted with a great many people. Only rarely did a pair of shoes fail to be handled by him at least once or twice. He resolved some, patched up others, and sometimes changed the tops. And often he could observe the work, for he was an expert cobbler, had good merchandise, was not too expensive and made delivery at the promised time. If he was able to deliver on the day agreed upon, he took the job; if not, he did not mislead customers but told them in advance. Everyone knew Avdieitch, and he had plenty of work.

At all times Avdieitch had been recognized as a decent fellow. But with advancing age, he began to think more about his soul and how better to communicate with God. He was still working for an employer when his wife died, leaving him a little boy three years old. He had previously lost the others, the older ones. First, he wanted to send his son to his sister's in the country. Then he took pity on him and thought: "It would be too hard on my little Kapitosha to live with a strange family. I want to keep him with me."

So Avdieitch quit his employer's service, set himself up in business and kept his son. But God did not bless Martin through his children. Kapitosha began to grow up and to help his father, and fortune seemed to smile on him. But suddenly he fell ill, took to his bed for one week and died.

Martin buried his child and was deeply despondent.

He was so depressed that he even began to rail against Providence; he was so unhappy that he frequently asked God to grant him the boon of death, and reproached Him for not having taken him, the old man, instead of his only son, his adored son. Avdieitch even stopped going to church.

One day about Pentecost, Avdieitch was paid a visit by one of his fellow countrymen, a pilgrim who had been wandering for eight years. They chatted, and Avdieitch complained bitterly about his misfortunes.

"I no longer even care about living, man of God," he said. "I am eager to die. That is all that I ask of the Lord. Now I no longer have any hope."

The little old man replied:

"It is wicked to talk that way, Martin. It is not incumbent on us to judge what God has done. Our intelligence cannot cope with it. God alone is the proper judge of what He has done. He has decided that you should live and that your son should die; undoubtedly it is better that way. And your despair is caused by the fact that you wish to live for yourself, for your own happiness."

"But how should one live?" Martin asked.

"How live for God? Christ has revealed the secret to us. Do you know how to read? Buy the Gospels and read them. Through them you will learn how one should live for God; it is all written down."

These words impressed Avdieitch. That same day he bought a New Testament in large type and started to read it. He intended to read it only during holy days. But once he had commenced, he experienced such relief that he fell into the habit of reading a few pages each day. Sometimes he was so fascinated by what he was reading that all the oil in his lamp was consumed before he had been able to put aside his book.

Thus he read each evening; and the more he read, the more he understood clearly what God desired of him and how he had to live for Him. And more and more was his soul filled with joy.

Formerly, before he went to bed, he used to sigh and to moan as he evoked the memory of Kapitosha. Now he was content to say: "Glory to You! Glory to You, my God! It is Your will."

From this time onwards, Avdieitch's life changed completely. Formerly, on holidays, he was accustomed to enter a public house, to drink tea and even a glass of brandy. He relaxed with a friend and left the public house not drunk, but slightly gay, and began to mouth foolish statements and to address and insult passers-by.

But all that was now finished, and his life flowed along calmly and happily. He set to work at dawn, accomplished his chores, then took down his lamp, placed it on the table, took his book from the shelf, opened it and read. And the more he read, the more he understood, and his soul was at peace.

Once it happened that he stayed up reading even later than he did habitually. He was perusing the Gospel according to Saint Luke. In Chaper VI he read the following verses:

"And unto him that smiteth thee on the one cheek, offer also the other; and him that taketh away thy cloak forbid not to take thy coat also."

"Give to every man that asketh of thee; and of him that taketh away thy goods ask them not again."

"And as ye would that men would do to you, do ye also to them likewise."

Then he read other verses, in which the Lord said:

"And why call ye me Lord, Lord, and do not the things which I say?

"Whosoever cometh to me, and heareth my sayings, and doeth them, I will show you to whom he is like:

"He is like a man which built a house, and digged deep, and laid the foundation on a rock; and when the flood arose, the stream beat vehemently upon that house, and could not shake it; for it was founded upon a rock.

"But he that heareth, and doeth not, is like a man that without a foundation built a house upon the earth, against which the stream did beat vehemently, and immediately it fell; and the ruin of that house was great."

On reading this, Avdieitch's heart was overflowing with joy. He took off his glasses, placed them on the book, put his elbows on the table and remained pensive. He considered his own life in connection with the words and thought: "Is my house founded upon rock or upon sand? If it is on rock, it is a good life. One feels light-hearted when one is alone and acting according to God's commands. While if one allows oneself to be alienated from God, one can revert to a state of sin. I am going to continue. I feel extraordinarily well. May God help me!"

Having made this reflection, he wanted to retire. But he could not make up his mind to stop reading his book. So he settled down to renew his reading with the seventh chapter. He read the story of the centurion and the widow's son; he read Jesus' response to John's disciples. He came to the passage in which the rich Pharisee invited the Lord to dine at his house; he read how the woman who was a sinner rubbed His feet with oil and washed them with her tears, and how he forgave her her sins.

Coming to verse 44, he read:

"And he turned to the woman, and said unto Simon: Seest thou this woman? I entered into thine house, thou gavest me no water for my feet; but she hath washed my feet with tears, and wiped them with the hairs of her head.

"Thou gavest me no kiss; but this woman since the time I came in hath not ceased to kiss my feet.

"My head with oil thou didst not anoint; but this woman hath anointed my feet with ointment."

He read this verse and thought: "*You have not given me water for my feet; you have not kissed me; you have not anointed my head with oil.*"

And Avdieitch, again taking off his glasses, put down his book and reflected: "Probably that Pharisee was like me. I, too, have thought solely of myself when I drank my tea, thought that I was warm and lacked nothing. I did not think at all of my guest. I thought of myself alone and did not care about the other person. And who was the guest? The Lord Himself! If He had come to my house, would I then have acted in the same way?"

And Avdieitch, leaning on his two hands, fell asleep without being aware of it.

"Martin!" a voice suddenly said in his ear.

Martin awoke with a start. "Who is there?"

He turned around and looked in the direction of the door; no one. He fell asleep once more. Suddenly he distinctly heard these words:

"Martin, oh Martin! Look for me in the street tomorrow; I will be there."

Martin became fully conscious, rose from his chair and rubbed his eyes.

He could not make up his mind if he had heard these words in actuality, or if he had dreamed them. He extinguished his lamp and went to bed.

The next morning he arose before daylight, said his prayers, lit his stove, set some cabbage soup and some gruel to cooking, put his samovar to a boil, put on his apron and seated himself near the window to work.

All the while he worked, he thought about what had happened the night before and did not know what to conclude: had he been duped by an illusion, or had someone really spoken to him? "Such things do happen," he told himself.

Martin was there, working and looking out of the window. And when he noticed any boots with which he was not familiar, he leaned over so he could see through the window not only the feet but the face of the passer-by.

A doorman passed, wearing new felt boots, then the water carrier, then an old soldier of the time of Nicolas, shod with old patched-up boots and armed with a long shovel. Avdieitch had recognized him by his shoes.

He was named Stepanitch and lived with a shopkeeper of the village, who had taken him in as a charitable act. His responsibility was helping the doormen.

The old soldier set about clearing away the snow in front of Avdieitch's window. The latter looked at him, then went back to his work.

"How stupid I am to be on the look-out this way," thought Avdieitch, making fun of himself. "Stepanitch is clearing away the snow, and I think he is Christ who has come to see me. I am out of my mind, old idiot that I am."

Yet, after he had made a dozen more stitches with his needle, he looked through the window once more. He saw Stepanitch who, having leaned his shovel against the wall, was resting and warming himself.

"He is old, the poor man," thought Avdieitch. "It is apparent that he no longer has the strength even to clear away the snow. Perhaps I should offer him some tea; as it happens, my samovar is just about to grow cold."

He stuck his awl on the work bench, rose, placed the samovar on the table, poured some water in the teapot and knocked on the window. Stepanitch turned around and approached. Avdieitch signaled to him and went to open the door.

"Enter and warm yourself," he said to him. "You must be cold."

"May Christ bless you! Yes, it is true: my bones hurt," answered Stepanitch.

Stepanitch entered, shook off the snow, wiped his feet, lest he dirty the room, and reeled on his legs.

"Don't bother to wipe your feet; it doesn't matter; I will clean up. Come and sit down and drink a little tea," said Avdieitch.

He filled two glasses and pushed one over to his guest; he himself emptied his into a saucer and started to blow on it.

Stepanitch drank, turned over his glass, placed the remainder of his sugar on top of it, and thanked his host. But it was clear that he wanted some more.

"Another glass?" said Avdieitch.

And once again he filled the two glasses. Even while he drank, Avdieitch constantly looked at the street.

"Are you expecting someone?" Stepanitch asked him.

"Am I expecting someone? I am ashamed to tell you whom I am expecting. I do not know whether or not my expectations are justified, but something happened to me that made a strong impression on me... I do not know if it was real or a dream... Understand, my brother, that yesterday I was reading the Gospels of our little Father, Christ: learning how much he suffered, how he lived on the earth. You have certainly heard about these things, haven't you?"

"Yes, I have heard..." replied Stepanitch. "But all those like myself, poor ignorant souls, do not know how to read."

"Be that as it may, I was reading about how he lived on the earth. I read how he came to the house of the Pharisee and how the latter did not go to meet Him. Well, yesterday, just after I had read that, I wondered how best to honor our little Father, Christ. I said to myself: 'If such a thing happened to me, I would not even know how to honor Him adequately, just as he, the Pharisee, did not welcome Him properly!' I was reflecting along these lines when I dozed off. And as I was napping, brother, somehow or other I heard a voice calling me by name. I rose; the voice seemed to murmur to me: "Wait for me, it said. I shall come tomorrow." And it repeated this twice in succession, Well, believe it or not, all of that remains crystal-clear in my mind. I try to rationalize in vain; in spite of everything, I am constantly expecting Him, Him who is our Father!"

Stepanitch nodded without saying anything. He finished his tea and set his glass on the saucer. But Avdieitch picked it up once again and poured him some tea.

"Drink it, it will do you good. I imagine that He, our Father, never rebuffed anyone when He lived on the earth, and that he invariably sought out the humble. He always visited the lowly people. And He chose His disciples from among persons like us,n fishermen and laborers. "So the last shall be first," he said, and the first last... You called me, Lord, and I wash your feet. He who would be first must be the servant of others." He also said: "Blessed are the poor in spirit, the meek and the merciful."

Stepanitch had forgotten his tea. He was a sensitive oldster. He listened, and tears rolled down his face.

"Oh, please have some more," Avdieitch said to him.

But Stepanitch made the sign of the cross, thanked him, pushed back the glass and rose.

"I thank you, Martin Avdieitch, for having received me as you have," he said, "and for having nourished both my soul and my body."

"At your service. Until we meet again. I am always happy when someone comes to see me," Avdieitch responded.

Stepanitch left. Martin poured himself the remaining tea, drank it, removed the dishes, then once again seated himself near the window and picked up a heel.

He sewed, and even as he sewed, he looked out of the window and waited for Christ. He could think of nothing but Him and his acts, and the different words of Christ echoed and re-echoed in his head.

Two soldiers passed. One was wearing regulation boots, the other his own boots. Then came a gentleman in shiny galoshes, and after that a baker with his basket. Finally, there passed by the window a woman in woollen stockings and a peasant's shoes. She passed by the window and stopped up against the wall. Avdieitch bent over to look at her. He saw, leaning against the wall and turning her back to the wind, a stranger, poorly clothed, with an infant in her arms. She was trying to shelter her baby, but in vain, for she had nothing in which to wrap him. The woman was wearing dirty summer clothes.

Through the window, Avdieitch heard the infant cry and his mother try to comfort him, but without success. He rose, opened his door, went out and called up the stairs:

"Good woman! Oh, good woman!"

The stranger heard him and turned toward him.

"Why are you staying out in the cold with your child? Come in my place, where you will be better able to tend to him... This way! This way!"

The woman, taken by surprise, perceived an old man, in an apron and wearing glasses, who was signaling her to follow him. She did so. She descended the stairs and entered the room.

The old man led the woman near the bed. "Here, come over here," he said to her. "Sit down nearer the stove. Warm yourself and nurse your little one."

"But it happens that I have no more milk," she replied. "I myself have not eaten anything since the morning."

Nevertheless she offered her breast to the child.

Avdieitch shook his head. He approached the table, took some bread, a bowl, opened the stove, in which cabbage was cooking, took out the pot of gruel. But as it was not yet cooked, he put only the cabbage soup in the bowl and set it on the table. He cut some bread, took a napkin and set the table.

"Sit down, my good woman," he said, "and eat. I will take care of your child for a little while. I too have had children, and I know how to tend them."

The woman made the sign of the cross, then sat down at the table and ate, while Avdieitch, seated on the bed with the child, blew him kisses to comfort him. As the child continued to cry, Avdieitch pretended to threaten him with his finger, that he alternately pointed to his lips and drew back, but without putting it in his mouth, for the finger was black with wax. The child, his eyes focused on the finger, stopped crying and even started to laugh. Avdieitch was altogether delighted.

As she ate, the woman related who she was and from where she came.

"I am the wife of a soldier," she said. "It is now eight months since he was shipped out, and since then I have had no news. I was working as a cook when I gave birth. Once I had the child, they did not wish to keep me on, and for the last three months I have been without a position. I have eaten up everything I had. I wanted to find a place as a wet nurse, but was unable to; they told me that I was too thin. Then I went to see a shopkeeper, and she promised to hire me. I thought that the arrangements would be made immediately, but I was told to come back in a week... And she lives very far away. I am at the end of my rope, and my poor little one, too, is exhausted. Fortunately, my landlady has taken pity on us and, in the name of Christ, lets us sleep in her house. Otherwise I don't know what would become of us."

Avdieitch sighed and asked:

"Have you no warm clothing?"

"No. Yesterday I pawned my last shawl for twenty kopecks."

The woman approached the bed and took the infant.

Avdieitch rose, headed for the wall, searched and brought back a greatcoat.

"Take this," he said. "It's in bad condition, but it will always give you security."

The stranger looked at the garment, looked at the old man, took the greatcoat and burst into tears. Avdieitch turned aside, then went to his bed, took out a small chest, opened it, looked in it and came to sit down again facing the woman.

"May Christ be your salvation, Grandfather!" said the woman. "It was undoubtedly He who led me in front of your window. Except for that, my child would have frozen. When I started on the road, it was warm, and now, what cold! He indeed had a blessed inspiration, our Savior, when he led you to look out of the window and to take pity on me!"

Avdieitch smiled.

"It is *He,* as a matter of fact, who inspired me with the notion," he said. "It was not altogether by chance that I was looking out of the window."

And Martin told the woman about his dream, how he had heard a voice, and how the Lord had promised to come visit him that very day.

"Anything is possible," observed the woman. She rose, took the garment, wrapped the infant in it, saluted and thanked Avdieitch.

"Take this, in the name of Christ," he said, slipping into her hand a twenty-kopeck piece. "Use it to take the shawl out of hock."

The woman made the sign of the cross. Avdieitch did the same, then escorted her to the door. And the woman departed.

After having eaten his cabbage soup, Avdieitch set to work. Even while manipulating his awl, he did not take his eyes from the window; and each time that a profile cast a shadow, he lifted his eyes to see who was passing. He was acquainted with some of those who passed and not with others, but there was nothing out of the ordinary about them. One moment he saw an old woman, a traveling peddler who held in her hands a small apple basket, stop just outside his window. There were hardly any apples in the basket; she must have sold the others. On her back she carried a sack of small pieces of wood, probably collected at some construction site, with which she was undoubtedly returning home. Tired, presumably, she wanted to shift the sack to the other shoulder. She put it on the ground, put the sack of apples on a beam and piled up the sticks of wood. While she was thus occupied, a lad in a torn cap, come from who knew where, grabbed an apple from the basket and tried to escape. But the old woman had noticed the theft. She turned around and grasped the lad by the sleeve. The boy struggled to free himself, but she held onto him with two hands, snatched off his cap and pulled his hair. The lad roared, and the woman yelped. Avdieitch, without taking the time to fasten his awl, threw it on the ground and ran to the door. In his haste, he stumbled on the stairs and let his glasses fall. He rushed into the street. The old woman was still pulling the boy's hair, scolding him in no uncertain terms and threatening to take him to the police.

The child continued to struggle and yelled:

"I didn't take anything! Why are you beating me? Let me go!"

Avdieitch tried to separate them. He took the child by the hand and said:

"Let him go, Grandmother; forgive him, in the name of Christ."

"I'm going to forgive him so thoroughly that he will remember it until his next beating. I am going to take him to the police station, the good-for-nothing."

Avdieitch implored the old lady:

"Let him go, Grandmother; he won't do it again. Let him go, in the name of Christ."

The old woman released him. The lad was going to dash off, but Avdieitch retained him.

"Now ask the woman to forgive you, and don't repeat your action in the future, for I saw you take the apple."

The child started to cry and begged forgiveness.

"Fine. And now, here is an apple."

Avdieitch took an apple from the basket and held it out to the child.

"I am going to pay you for it, Grandmother," he told the old lady.

"You will spoil the naughty rascal," she observed. "He should have been recompensed in a manner that he would remember for at least a week."

"Oh, Grandmother, Grandmother, we may think along those

lines, but God judges things differently. If we deem it fitting to whip him for an apple, what should happen to us, to you and me, to punish us for our sins?"

The old woman was silent. And Avdieitch commenced to narrate for her the parable of the creditor who forgave a debtor his debt, and of the debtor who tried to kill his benefactor.

The old woman listened, and the lad also.

"God orders us to forgive," continued Avdieitch; "otherwise we should not deserve to be forgiven ourselves... to forgive everyone, and especially those who know not what they do."

The old woman nodded and sighed.

"If it is thus," she agreed... "But children are already only too disposed to do mischief."

"Then it is up to us, their elders, to teach them to do good."

"That is what I believe, too," the old woman assented. "I myself had seven children; only one daughter is left..."

And the old woman began to recount how she lived in her daughter's home, how she had grandchildren.

"You can see how feeble I am," she said, "and yet I work. My grandchildren... I become sentimental about them, they are so darling; you should see how they run to meet me. As for Axutka, there is one who will go with no one but me. Grandmother, she says, my good grandmother."

The old woman was overcome by emotion.

"Certainly he is only a child... May God protect him," said the old lady, turning toward the lad.

But as she was about to heave the sack on her shoulders again, the boy ran forward and said:

"Give it to me, Grandmother; I will carry it for you. It is on my way."

The old woman nodded and gave him the sack. And both of them went off side by side. The old woman had even neglected to collect from Avdieitch the price of the apple. Avdieitch, who remained alone, watched them depart, chatting. He followed them with his eyes, then re-entered his room, found his glasses, still intact, on the stairs, picked up his awl and once more set to work. He toiled for a while, but he could no longer see too clearly; just then he

128

noticed the lamplighter. "It is time to light my lamp," he said to himself. He prepared his little lamp, hung it up and resumed working. He finished one boot and examined it; it was a good job. He gathered up his tools, swept away the shavings, unhooked the lamp, that he placed on the table, and took the Gospels from the plank.

He wanted to start reading at the page where he had left off the evening before, but by chance he opened to another page.

As he opened the Gospels, he recalled the dream he had had the night before, and just at that moment he thought he heard a movement behind him. He turned around. He seemed to see some people, but he could not perceive them clearly. And a voice murmured in his ear:

"Martin, oh Martin, do you not recognize me?"

"Who are you?" asked Avdieitch.

"But it is me!" said the voice. "It is me!"

And Stepanitch, emerging from the shadows, smiled on him, dissipated like a cloud and disappeared.

"And it is me, too!" said another voice.

And from a dark corner emerged the woman with the child. The woman smiled, the infant smiled, and then both of them disappeared.

"And it is me also!" said a third voice.

And the old woman appeared, together with the boy holding an apple. The old lady and the boy smiled, then vanished.

And Avdieitch was overcome with joy. He made the sign of the cross, put on his glasses and took up the reading of the Gospels at the page to which he had opened.

At the top of the page he read:

"... For I was hungry, and ye gave me food to eat; I was thirsty, and ye gave me to drink; I was a stranger, and ye took Me in."

And at the bottom of the page:

"I say unto you verily that, inasmuch as ye have done these things for one of the least of these my brethren, ye have done them unto Me."

Then Avdieitch understood that in truth he had not been deceived by the dream, that the Lord had indeed come to visit him that day, and that it was He whom he had taken in.

The three old men

The archbishop of the city of Archangel was sailing toward the monastery of Solovki. On the same ship were some pilgrims who were on their way to see the holy relics. The wind was favorable, the weather fine, and there were no high waves to rock the boat.

Certain of the pilgrims were lying down; others were eating; others, seated in small groups, were chatting with one another. The archbishop, too, came on the deck to walk back and forth. In the front, a small group of the faithful had assembled; one of them, a peasant, was speaking, his hand extended toward the sea, and the others were listening to him.

The archbishop halted and looked in the direction the peasant was indicating. Nothing could be seen save for the ocean gleaming in the sun. The archbishop approached the group and lent an ear. At the sight of him, the peasant bared his head and grew silent. The others, following his example, took off their caps out of respect for the archbishop.

"Do not inconvenience yourselves, my brothers," said the archbishop... "I came here so I, too, could hear what you are relating, my good fellow."

"My word, the little fisherman was telling us the story of the three old men," said a peddler who was less timid than the others.

"Oh? And just exactly what was he telling you?" asked the archbishop.

He went toward the rail and seated himself on a chest.

"Continue," he added. "I, too, should like to listen to you. What were you pointing out that way, my friend?"

"Why, the small island that you can observe yonder," replied the little peasant, indicating a spot on the horizon, to the right." It was on that very island that the old men found salvation."

"But just where is your island?" demanded the archbishop.

"Will you please look in the direction of my hand... Do you see that little cloud? Well, it is a little lower ... to the left ... it looks like a gray band."

The archbishop scanned the horizon in vain; unaccustomed to the light, he could distinguish nothing on the sea gleaming in the sunshine.

"I don't see it," he said. "But who are these old men? How do the live? How have they found salvation?"

"They are men of God," the peasant responded. "I had heard them spoken of for a very long time, but I had never had the opportunity to see them. Then, last summer, I saw them."

And the fisherman recommenced his narrative... One day, as he was going fishing, he was blown against the island and perceived a tiny grotto and, nearby, an old man, who was immediately followed by two others. They fed him, hung his clothes up to dry and helped him to repair his boat.

"What did they look like?" demanded the archbishop.

"One was small, bent over and very old. He was clothed in an old cassock and appeared to be over a hundred years old. The white hairs of his beard were beginning to turn greenish. He was as smiling and serene as an angel in heaven. The second was slightly taller and also old; he wore a caftan with holes, and his bushy gray beard had yellow highlights. He was very vigorous; he turned over my boat as if it were a bucket before I even had time

132

to come to his aid. He, too, was cheerful. The third was very tall; his beard, as white as a swan, came down to his knees. He was sad, his eyelashes bristling above his eyes. His only garment was a loincloth of braided bark."

"And what did they say to you?" asked the archbishop.

"Oh, they did everything without saying very much; they spoke very little even among themselves. With a single look each could understand the other. I asked the big one if they had lived there for very long; he knitted his brows and muttered something in an annoyed tone. But the little old man immediately took his hand and smiled, and the big chap was quiet. And the little old man merely said to me: "Please pardon us,' and smiled."

While the peasant was speaking, the ship had approached a group of islands.

"You can now see it very distinctly," said the peddler. "May Your Eminence deign to look," he added, extending his hand.

The archbishop looked. He indeed perceived a black band; it was the little island. He looked for a long time; then, going from the prow to the stern, he addressed the pilot.

"What is the island that we can see yonder?"

"It has no name. There are a great many like that in this area."

"Is what they say true: that some old men have found salvation there?"

"It is rumored, Your Eminence, but I do not know if it is true. Fishermen swear they have seen them, but people often speak without rhyme or reason."

"I should like to land on that island and see the old men," said the archbishop. "Is that possible?"

"It cannot be done with this ship," said the pilot. "You need a dinghy to land there. It would be necessary to ask the captain."

The archbishop summoned the captain.

"I should like to see the old men," the archbishop told him. "Can you not take me there?"

The captain tried to dissuade him from undertaking the project.

"It would be possible, but we should lose a great deal of time. I would take the liberty of saying to your Eminence that visiting them is really not worth the trouble. I should even go so far as to say that the old men are stupid, that they do not understand anything, and that they don't know how to speak any better than the fish in the sea."

"I still should like to see them. I will pay any costs you incur. Please take me there."

Further objections were pointless. They made the necessary preparations; they changed the sails, and the pilot tacked in the direction of the island. They brought a chair for the archbishop to the bow, and he sat down and looked. All of the passengers assembled at the bow so that they, too, could look at the island. Those who had a good view could already distinguish the rocks and showed the grotto to the others. Soon one of them even caught sight of the three old men.

The captain fetched the field glasses, put them to his eyes and then offered them to the archbishop.

"As a matter of fact," he said, "there is a large stone to the right on the shore, and you can see three men."

In his turn the archbishop trained the field glasses in the indicated direction and looked through them. He could indeed perceive three men: one very tall, another smaller, and the third very tiny. They were standing on the shore and holding each other's hands.

"It is here, Your Eminence, that the ship must stop," the captain came over to say to the archbishop. "If you are willing, you can get into the dinghy, and we will wait for you here, at anchor." They weighed anchor, took in the sails, and the ship was stabilized. The dinghy was lowered into the water, the rowers jumped into it, and the archbishop descended into it by means of a small ladder. He seated himself on a bench toward the back of the dinghy, and the rowers headed the boat toward the island. Soon they were a mere stone's throw away. The three old men could be clearly distinguished: the one very tall and completely naked save for a loincloth of braided bark; another somewhat smaller, in a torn caftan; and a very tiny oldster, bent over and wearing an old cassock.

The three were all holding each other's hands.

The rowers reached the bank and touched land. The archbishop alit on the ground, blessed the old men, who saluted him piously, then spoke to them.

"I have learned that you have found salvation here, disciples of God," he said to them, "and that you pray to Christ to have, compassion on your fellow men. And since by the grace of God, I, His unworthy servant, have been called upon to minister unto His flock, I resolved that I would come to see you, you who also serve the Lord, and would bring you, if I could, the good word of God!"

The old men remained silent and looked at him smilingly.

"Tell me how you have found salvation and how you serve God," continued the archbishop.

The old man in the middle sighed and cast his eyes on the tiny little old man. The big oldster's face clouded over, and he, too, looked at the tiny old man. The latter smiled and said:

"Servant of God, we can serve only ourselves by earning our daily bread."

"But in that case, how do you pray?" asked the archbishop.

"This is our prayer: "You are three, we are three... Let us be the recipients of Your grace."

As soon as the little old man had pronounced these words, all three lifted their eyes toward heaven and repeated: "You are three, we are three... Let us be the recipients of Your grace."

The archbishop smiled and said:

"It is the Holy Trinity, about which you must know. But that is not the way to pray. Good old men, I have become fond of you; I see that you wish to please the Lord, but you do not know how properly to serve Him. That is not the way one should pray. I am going to teach you. Listen to me. It is not I who invented what I am about to teach you; it is in God's Holy Scriptures, where the Lord taught everyone how he should pray."

Then the archbishop explained to them how the Lord revealed Himself to men; he explained to them the Holy Trinity: God the father, God the son, God the Holy Ghost, and he added:

"God the son came on the earth to save the human race, and here is how he taught everyone to pray. Listen and repeat after me."

And the archbishop began:

"Our Father..."

One of the old men repeated:

"Our Father..."
The second old man repeated:
"Our Father..."
The third old man repeated:
"Our Father..."
"Who art in heaven..."
And the old men repeated:
"Who art in heaven..."

But the old man who was in the middle was confused: he substituted one word for the other. The big oldster could not continue, either; his moustaches covered his mouth. And the tiny old man, who no longer had any teeth, articulated very badly.

The archbishop again started the prayer from the beginning; the old men repeated after him. The archbishop sat down on a stone; the old men surrounded him, watched the movements of his lips and echoed what he said. Thus did the archbishop spend the entire day until evening, repeating with them as many as ten, twenty and a hundred times the same word, that the old men would say after him. They became confused; he again took up the litany and made them start over.

The archbishop refused to leave the old men until he had taught them the Lord's Prayer. They recited it with him, then by themselves. The old man in the middle, who had learned it before the other two, repeated it by himself. After that the archbishop made him repeat it alone several times, and the other two said it after him.

The night was already falling and the moon was rising from the sea by the time the archbishop rose to depart. He said goodbye to the old men, who bowed low, touching the ground. He helped them up, embraced each of them, told them to pray as he had instructed them, and seated himself on the little bench of the dinghy, which the rowers steered toward the big ship.

While the dinghy was making its way toward the ship, he could still hear the three old men, reciting aloud the Lord's Prayer. Soon the dinghy drew close to the ship. He could no longer hear the voices of the old men, but he could perceive the three of them on the bank, illuminated by the moonlight. The tiny old man was in the middle, the big one to his right, the third to his left.

They reached the ship. The archbishop climbed onto the deck. They lifted anchor, let out the sails, that were swelled by the wind, and the ship resumed its voyage. The archbishop walked to the stern and sat down there, his gaze fixed on the island. At first the old men were still visible; then they disappeared, and he could see only the island. Soon the island disappeared as well, and he could no longer see anything but the sea, that shone as moonbeams played on it.

The pilgrims went to bed. The deck grew silent. But the archbishop was not yet ready to go to sleep. Remaining alone at the stern, he gazed at the sea, at the spot where the island had disappeared, and thought about the good old men. He recalled their joy on learning the prayer, and he thanked God for having chosen him to bring the light of His word to the venerable old men.

Thus did the archbishop reflect, his eyes fixed on the sea, on the spot where the island had disappeared. His eyes bothered him: light appeared on the waves, sometimes here, sometimes there. Was it a sea gull or a white sail? He looked more intently and thought: "It is a boat, a sailboat that is following us. But how rapidly it glides! A while ago it was far off, very far, and now it is already very near. And it is a strange sort of boat. The sail does not look... like a sail... Yet something is pursuing us, catching up to us..." But the archbishop could not distinguish the thing clearly. "Is it a boat, a bird, a fish? It could be a man, but it is too big for a man, and besides, a man would not be able to walk on the sea."

The archbishop rose, went to find the pilot and said to him:

"What is that, my brother? Really, what is it?"

But he himself now saw distinctly that it was the three old men who were running on the surface of the sea, their white beards gleaming, and who were approaching the ship.

The pilot, who had turned around, let go of the tiller in terror and exclaimed:

"Lord, the old men are pursuing us over the water! They are running just as if they were on dry land!"

Hearing his cries, the passengers rose and rushed to the rear. There, all of them could see the old men running, holding each other by the hand, and those on the sides signaled to the ship to stop. The three of them were running on the water as if on land, without moving their legs.

Before there was time to stop the ship, the old men had overtaken it. They lifted their heads and said in chorus:

"Servant of God, we have forgotten what you taught us. As long as we kept repeating it, we remembered it, but an hour after we ceased repeating it, we forgot one word and then absolutely everything. We no longer recall anything at all. Teach us once more."

The archbishop made the sign of the cross, leaned toward the old man and said:

"Ancients of the Lord, in spite of that, your prayers will ascend to God. It is not up to me to instruct you. Rather, you should pray for the rest of us, poor sinners that we are."

And the archbishop saluted them, bowing low to the ground. For a moment the old men remained motionless; then they turned around and departed over the sea.

And until morning, a bright light was visible in the direction where they had disappeared.

Is much land needed for a man?

The elder sister, who lived in the city, came to the country to visit her sister. The older girl had married a shopkeeper in the city; the younger, a peasant who lived in the country. The sisters drank tea and chatted. The older praised her existence in town. She recounted how well she lived there, what good food she had, and how she went for walks, to parties and to the theater.

The younger sister, annoyed, began to denigrate a tradesman's life and to wax enthusiastic about her own, the life of a peasant. "I would not exchange my existence for yours," she said. "It is true that our lives, the lives of peasants, may be dull, but we know no fear. Your life is more sophisticated, but sometimes you earn a great deal, and sometimes you lose everything. Today you are rich; tomorrow you will be begging for alms. Our existence, a peasant's existence, is more secure. A peasant has a narrower life, but a longer one. We will never be rich, but we will always have enough to eat."

"Yes, but while living with pigs and calves," answered the older.

"You'll have neither fine manners nor luxury, despite all of your husband's work; you will remain on a dunghill and you will die on one in the end, and the same fate will await your children."

"Undoubtedly!" agreed the younger. "Our occupation is responsible for that. But on the other hand, we live independent lives. We do not grovel before anyone, we do not fear anyone. You who reside in the city are exposed to temptation. Today everything may be fine. But tomorrow the devil will come to tempt your husband with cards, brandy and women, and everything will go very badly. Do such things not happen to you?"

On the stove, the husband, Pakhom, was listening to the chatter of the women.

"It is really the truth," he said. "Those of us who turn over the earth that nourishes us from childhood do not think about vain frivolities. The only trouble is that we have too little land. But if I had as much land as I wanted, then I should not be afraid of anyone, not even the devil."

After they had drunk their tea, the women discussed clothes some more, put the dishes away, then left to go to bed.

The devil, seated behind the door, had heard everything. He was well pleased that the peasant's wife had encouraged her husband to confront him. Had he not boasted, indeed, that if he had a great deal of land, the devil himself would not be able to overcome him? "That's fine," he thought. "It's between the two of us! I will give you a great deal of land, and thereby I will trap you."

The peasant had a neighbor who was a little property owner, a woman who possessed twenty deciares of land. She had good relations with the peasants and did no harm to anyone; but as manager she hired a former soldier who began to inflict fines on the peasants. In spite of all of the precautions taken by Pakhom, sometimes it was his horse that trespassed on the oat fields, sometimes a cow that wandered into the garden or calves that found their way into the meadow. And for each offense there was a fine.

Pakhom paid, swore and struck out at his family. All summer long he suffered at the manager's hands; therefore he was happy when the time came to bring in the livestock, even though he had to feed them, for at least he was no longer afraid. During the course of the winter, the rumor spread that the proprietor was selling her land and that a peasant who lived beside the highway wanted to buy it.

The peasants went to see the property owner to ask that she not sell to the other peasant but to them. They guaranteed her a higher price. The property owner agreed. The peasants arranged to have the property bought by the *mir* (a village community of peasant farmers). They had one, then two meetings, but the project was not going forward. The devil was making them hostile, so that they could not come to an agreement. Finally they decided that each one should buy his own portion, based on his resources. The property owner was in accord. Pakhom learned that his neighbor had bought twenty deciares and that the property owner had granted him the option of paying half of the cost in installments. Pakhom was overcome by jealousy. "They will buy all the land," he thought, "and I will have nothing."

He discussed it with his wife.

"The people are buying," he said. "We, too, are going to have to buy ten deciares or so; else we won't be able to earn a living. That manager has ruined us with his fines."

He thought over the means of concluding the sale. He had a hundred rubles in savings. By selling his colt and half of his bees, hiring out his son as a farm worker and borrowing some more from his godfather, Pakhom could accumulate half the needed sum. He collected the money, chose a plot of fifteen deciares with a little woods and went to see the property owner to conclude the transaction. He purchased the fifteen deciares and, his business finished, left a deposit. They went to the city to draw up the bill of sale; he paid half in cash and committed himself to pay the balance within two years. Pakhom returned home a property owner.

He borrowed more grain. He sowed his new acquisition, and the harvest was good. Within a single year he paid the former owner and his brother-in-law what he owed them. Thus did Pakhom become a true landed proprietor. It was his own land that he tilled and sowed; it was on his own land that he mowed hay; on his own land that he raised livestock; the trees on his own land that he cut into posts. When Pakhom tilled his land, saw his wheat and his

grassland grown, he was ecstatic. The grass seemed exceptional to him, the flowers somehow different. Formerly, when he walked over the land, it had appeared to him to be ordinary land; now, in his eyes, it was transformed.

Thus did Pakhom live and rejoice in his good fortune. Everything was going very well. But suddenly peasants began playing havoc with Pakhom's wheat fields and meadows. In vain he begged them to desist; they continued. Sometimes the shepherds allowed the sheep to enter the meadows; sometimes the horses trampled the wheat. Pakhom chased them away and forgave them; he did not want to resort to the law. Nevertheless, he finally lost patience and complained to the village court of law. He knew perfectly well that the peasants were not acting as they were through maliciousness, but because they themselves were cramped for space. He thought: "Still, I cannot continue to forgive them; otherwise they will take everything from me. I must make an example of them."

He made a first example, then a second: one was penalized by a fine, also another. The neighboring peasants became worked up over the situation. It came to pass that they purposely sent animals to graze on his land. One night someone entered the little woods and cut down about ten linden trees to make adzes. As he crossed the woods, Pakhom noticed something white. He approached and saw some stripped trees on the ground; in the earth there remained only the stumps. If he had cut down only the trees at the edge, if he had at least spared one tree! But the rogue had destroyed all of them. Pakhom was outraged. "Oh, if I knew who the guilty person is, I would seek vengeance!" he thought. He sought and sought to find out whom to blame. "It can't be anyone but Simon," he decided. He went to look in Simon's barnyard but could find nothing. He quarreled with Simon and was more convinced than ever that he was the culprit. He denounced him to the authorities. They were summoned to appear in court. Evidence was presented and heard, and the peasant was acquitted for lack of proof.

Pakhom's irritation intensified. He fulminated against the village elder and the judge.

"You people are in league with criminals," he told them. "If you were doing your duty, you would not set thieves free."

Pakhom was angry both with the judges and with his neighbors. They ended by threatening him with arson. Then Pakhom could live freely on his land, but would be looked on askance by the peasants and would feel himself isolated in the community.

There was a rumor that people were migrating to new areas. Pakhom thought: "I have no need to leave my land, but if some of the others so away, we will have more room here. I can take their land and add it to mine, and I will live better, for I constantly feel cramped here."

One day when Pakhom was in the house, a wayfarer, a peasant, entered his dwelling. He was allowed to spend the night there, he was given food to eat, and he was asked where God was leading him. The peasant replied that he had come from the south, from the Volga, that he had worked there. Going into detail, the peasant recounted how people had migrated there. His family settled there, enrolled in the commune, and were allocated ten deciares per person. He added:

"And the earth there is so rich that the rye that is sown produces ears so high and so thick that one can no longer see the horses. Five fistfuls of ears, and you have a sheaf. A poverty-stricken peasant, who arrived with empty hands, now has six horses and two cows."

Pakhom, his pulse pounding, thought: "So why should I remain here, cramped for space, when I could live better elsewhere? I will sell all that I possess here, and with the money I will build in that region and settle there. To live here, cramped for room, is really a sin. Only I should go to examine the situation for myself."

Toward summer, he made ready and departed. He descended the Volga in a steamboat until he reached Samara; then he covered four hundred versts on foot and arrived at his destination. He had been told the truth. The peasants lived comfortably; the commune welcomed newcomers and gave each person ten deciares; and he who had some money could, in addition to the land ceded to him for a fixed period, buy in perpetuity, at a cost of three rubles a deciare, some excellent land.

Pakhom gathered all the information and returned to his home toward autumn. He set about selling all of his possessions. He made a profitable sale of his land, he sold his house and his livestock, resigned from the rolls of the commune and, when spring came, departed with his family for their new location.

Pakhom arrived in his new country with his family and registered in the commune of a large village. As a new resident, he paid the village elders and put all his papers in order. Pakhom was welcomed. He was given, since there were five persons, fifty deciares of land, in different fields, without counting the grazing grounds. Pakhom built his house and acquired some livestock. Taking account only of the land he had been given, he now owned three times as much as he had formerly. And his land was fertile. His life was ten times as beautiful as it had been previously. He had as much grazing ground and tillable land as he wanted; he could have as much livestock as he desired.

At the beginning, while he was building and getting settled, everything seemed wonderful to him. But after a while, he found that on this land he was as cramped as before. Pakhom wished to sow wheat. Wheat could be sowed in virgin earth, where the feathery stalks would grow, or else in fallow land. The earth was cultivated for one or two years, then abandoned until the stalks grew again. There was an abundance of loose earth, but only rye could be sown in it; wheat required solid earth. And the potential buyers of solid earth were numerous. There was not enough for everyone, and they argued over it. The wealthiest wanted to till it themselves; the poorest sold it to merchants to pay their taxes. Pakhom was eager to sow a great deal. The following year, he went to a merchant and leased the land for a year.

He sowed some more grain, and everything grew nicely, but it was far from the village, at least fifteen versts away. Pakhom realized that in that region peasant merchants had country houses and that they waxed rich. "I would be like them" he thought, "if I could buy land in perpetuity and build country houses, I could have everything near at hand."

And he reflected on how he might acquire land in perpetuity.

Thus did Pakhom live for three years. He leased land and sowed wheat. They were good years: he produced a respectable wheat crop, and he made money. He could well have lived peacefully, but he was upset that he had to lease the land every year. "It is too much trouble," he thought. "As soon as land is proven to be good, a peasant hastens to take it. And if I don't arrive in time, I have no place where I can sow." Another time he had leased some land to some peasants; he had already tilled it when the peasants went to court to claim it, and all of his labor was wasted. "If I owned all of my own land, I would not have to defer to anyone, and everything would be fine." Pakhom researched sites where he might buy land in perpetuity. He found a peasant who had five hundred deciares; he was in dire financial straits and was selling cheaply. Pakhom entered into negotiations with him and discussed the matter. They ended by agreeing on fifteen hundred rubles, half in cash and the balance in term payments. The arrangements had all been made when one day a passerby, a merchant, stopped at Pakhom's house to feed his horses. They drank tea and chatted. The merchant stated that he had just come from the Baschkirs' region. He said that there he had bought five thousand deciares of land for only a thousand rubles. Pakhom questioned him, and the merchant replied:

"All I had to do was grease the palms of the elders: I gave them gifts of robes and rugs for a hundred or so rubles, a chest full of tea, and I offered to let them drink like fishes. So I was able to buy for twenty kopecks a deciare."

He showed the deed of sale and continued:

"The land is situated near a little river, and feathery stalks grow throughout the area."

Pakhom was tireless in asking about the why's and the how's.

"You couldn't make the circuit of the land on foot in a whole year," the merchant said. "All of it belongs to the Baschkirs, and those simple souls are as stupid as geese. You could even have it for nothing."

"Ah," thought Pakhom, "why buy five hundred deciares for a thousand rubles and go into debt into the bargain if for that same sum I could have Lord knows how much acreage?"

Pakhom inquired about directions, and as soon as he had seen the merchant off, he made preparations to depart. He left the house in the care of his wife and left with his helper. First they went to the city to buy a chest of tea, presents, wine, everything that the merchant had mentioned; then they departed. They had already covered five hundred versts when, on the seventh day, they arrived at an encampment of the Baschkirs. The merchant had spoken the truth. They all lived on the steppes near a little river, in woolen tents. They did not work the fields and did not eat bread, but paraded their horses and their cattle on the steppe. The foals were tied up behind the tents; twice a day their mothers were brought to them; they milked the mares, and made kumiss from their milk. The women whipped the kumiss and made cheese from it. The men did nothing but drink kumiss (fermented milk) and tea, eat mutton and play the flute. All of them were fat, gay, with shiny skins, and caroused all summer long. These people were altogether ignorant; they did not know Russian, but they were exceedingly amiable.

When they espied Pakhom, the Baschkirs came out of their tents and surrounded him. Among them there was an interpreter.

Pakhom informed them that he had come to acquire some land. The Baschkirs greeted him warmly and bade him enter a pretty tent. They seated him on some rugs, placed down cushions over him and offered him tea and kumiss. They killed a sheep and invited him to eat.

Pakhom got the gifts that were in his wagon and distributed them to the Baschkirs; he drank tea with them. The Baschkirs appeared to be beside themselves with delight. For a long time they jabbered to one another, then ordered the interpreter to translate.

"They have asked me to say that they have grown very fond of you," said the interpreter," and that it is our custom to treat our guests as hospitably as possible and to exchange present for present. You have offered us gifts. Tell us what pleases you, and we will give it to you in exchange."

"It is principally your land that attracts me," responded Pakhom. "At home we are cramped for space, for land is lacking and used up, whereas you have plenty of land, and good land at that. I have never seen any to equal it."

The interpreter translated Pakhom's words. The Baschkirs talked and talked. Pakhom did not understand what they were saying, but he could see that they were good-humored, shouted something and laughed. Finally they became silent and looked at Pakhom, and the interpreter said to him:

"They ask me to say that in appreciation of your generosity, they are delighted to let you have as much land as you wish. Only indicate with your finger the plot that you desire, and it will be yours."

The Baschkirs again began speaking, discussing something among themselves.

"What are they saying?" asked Pakhom.

"Some of them are saying that this matter should be referred to the chief," the interpreter answered simply, "that without his consent the thing is not possible. The others say that they do not need his approval."

While they were thus debating, suddenly there appeared a man wearing a fox hat. Everyone was quiet and rose.

"It is the chief," announced the interpreter.

Pakhom immediately took the finest garment he had and presented it to the chief, along with five pounds of tea. The chief accepted them and took his place at the head of the group. Without making him wait, the Baschkirs explained the matter at hand. The chief listened intently. With his head he signaled them to be quiet and began to speak Russian to Pakhom.

"There is a great deal of land; take what you want," he said.

"Take as much as I want," thought Pakhom. "There should be a formal agreement; otherwise they can say, "It is yours," and take it back later."

So he answered the chief:

"I thank you for your kind words. You have a great deal of land, and I do not need very much... Only I will have to know which plot is mine, delimit it and have a written deed. For we are all mortal. You who are giving me this land are good and honest men, but your children might take it back."

The chief laughed.

"So be it," he said... "Everything will be done in accordance with regulations."

Pakhom stretched out on the feather bed but could not fall asleep. He could not keep his mind off his land. "What a chore I have let myself in for!" he said to himself. "I am going to stake out a huge holding... In a day I can surely cover fifty versts; at this time of year a day is as long as a year. Fifty versts! How much land will that mean? I will procure steers to pull two wagons, I will hire helpers, I will cultivate the area that pleases me and let the cattle graze on the rest."

Pakhom could not sleep at all that night. He only dozed off a little before dawn, and at once he had a dream: he was lying in the same tent, and outside he heard someone burst out laughing. He wanted to know who was laughing like that. He rose, went out of the tent, and saw the chief of the Baschkirs seated in front of the tent, holding his stomach with his two hands and laughing until his sides hurt. He approached him and asked: "Why are you laughing?" Then he saw that the man was no longer the Baschkir chief, but the merchant who had previously come to his house and spoken to him about the land. He immediately asked the merchant if he had been there for a long time. But already the figure was no longer the merchant, but the peasant who came to see him. Then Pakhom perceived that it was no longer the peasant but the devil himself, with horns and cloven hoofs, who was exploding with laughter as he looked at something. "What is he looking at? Why is he laughing?" thought Pakhom. He approached in order to see better and perceived a man with bare feet, lying down, in a shirt and shorts, his face, exposed to the air, as white as a shroud. Then Pakhom looked at the man more intently and saw that it was he himself, and that he was dead.

Pakhom awoke in a panic. He roused himself, thinking: "One dreams all kinds of dreams!" He turned around and saw that it was already light. "It is time to awaken the others and leave," he thought.

Pakhom rose and awakened his servant, who was sleeping in the wagon, ordered him to harness his animals and went to awaken the Baschkirs.

The Baschkirs rose and foregathered. The chief came also. They began to drink kumiss and offered Pakhom tea. But Pakhom was afraid of being late.

"Since we have to go, let's go now. It is time," he said.

The Baschkirs assembled and left, some on horseback, some in wagons. Pakhom got into his wagon with his helper; they brought along a shovel. They arrived at the steppe. The dawn was beginning to break. They ascended a small hill *(schikhan* in Baschkir). The Baschkirs descended from their conveyances and gathered in a single group. The chief approached Pakhom and, pointing to the country with his hand, said to him:

"All that you see belongs to us. Choose the part that pleases you most."

Pakhom's eyes gleamed. As smooth as the palm of his hand, as black as the seeds of a poppy, the earth was covered with feathery stalks, and in the ravines there was grass of different sorts, grass as high as a man's chest.

The chief took off his fox hat, laid it on the ground and said:

"This is our landmark. Leave from here, and return here. All the ground you have covered will belong to you."

Pakhom took out his money, put it in the hat, and removed his caftan, keeping on only his tunic. He drew his belt more tightly, took a little sack containing bread, attached to his belt a small flask of water, straightened the tops of his boots, took the shovel that his helper was holding and was ready to depart. He wondered in what direction he should go. The land was promising everywhere. "It is good everywhere; I will go in the direction of the rising sun," he thought.

He headed in the direction of the sun and waited for it to rise. He thought: "I should not lose any time; it is easier to walk in the freshness of the new day."

The Baschkirs on horseback were also holding themselves in readiness, waiting to leave the hill after Pakhom. As soon as he observed the disk of the sun, Pakhom set off on the steppe.

Pakhom walked neither slowly nor rapidly. He walked one verst, stopped, dug a hole and put a stake in it. He continued on his way. Once he was warmed up, he accelerated his pace. After a certain distance, he dug and planted another marker. Pakhom turned around. He could see clearly the hill and the people who were there; the rim of a wheel shone in the sun.

Pakhom decided that he had already gone five versts. Feeling warm, he took off his tunic and put it on his shoulders; then he fastened his belt again and continued on his way. He walked

151

another five versts. It was warm. He looked at the sun. It was time for lunch. "Already a quarter of the day is over!" he thought. "But there are four quarters altogether. It is not yet time to return. I am only going to take off my boots."

He sat down, took off his boots, attached them to the back of his belt and set forth once more. He felt confortable and at ease and thought: "I am going to do another five versts, and then I will turn to the left. The earth is too rich; the farther I go, the better it is!"

He continued to walk straight ahead. He turned around and found he could barely see the hill. The people looked as black as ants. "Well," thought Pakhom, "I think I should go back on this side; I have already taken enough."

Pakhom was dripping with perspiration, and he was thirsty. He took his flask and drank as he walked. He stopped to plant still another marker and turned left. He walked and walked; the grass was high, and it was very warm.

Pakhom began to tire. He looked at the sun and saw that it was exactly dinner time. "Well," he thought," I should take a rest!"

Pakhom stopped, sat down, ate a little bread, drank some water, but did not lie down. "If I lie down," he thought, "I will fall asleep." He remained seated for a moment, took a deep breath and went on his way. At first he walked with a light and lively step; dinner had restored his strength. But it was very warm, and he grew very sleepy. Pakhom felt exhausted. But he thought: "Bah! One more hour of suffering, one century to enjoy myself."

Pakhom walked for a long while in the same direction. He was going to turn left when he noticed a new ravine. "It would be a shame to leave that one outside the limits; good flax should grow there." Therefore he continued to bear to the right, included the ravine that way, planted a stake and made a second detour. He turned back toward the hill. He could barely make out the men there. "Oh," he thought, "I have gone too far along the first two sides; I am going to have to make this one shorter!"

He skirted the third side, quickening his steps. He looked at the sun, that was on the point of setting. As yet he had gone only two versts along the third side, while his destination was still about fifteen versts away. "My land will be shaped irregularly," he thought, "but I have to go directly to the finish line. There is already enough land as it is." And Pakhom speedily dug a hole and turned right toward the hill.

He walked straight toward the hill. He felt very fatigued. His feet hurt him, for they were covered with bruises, and he was completely worn out. He wanted to take a break but he dared not, since that would prevent him from reaching his destination before the sun set. The sun would not wait. He went down and down. "Alas," Pakhom thought, "perhaps I made a mistake; I must have made too wide a circuit. What will become of me if I don't arrive in time?"

Sometimes he looked at the hill, sometimes at the sun. It was still a far distance to his goal, and the sun was descending rapidly. Pakhom began to run. The flesh of his feet was raw, but he ran nevertheless. He ran and ran, but was still far from his destination. He threw away his tunic, his boots, his flask, his hat; he kept only the shovel, on which he leaned. "Oh," he thought, "I was too much of a glutton; I have lost everything. I will never arrive before the sun sets!"

To his horror, he was out of breath. He ran, sweat plastering his shirt and shorts to his body, his mouth dry. His chest heaved like a blacksmith's bellows; his heart was beating like a hammer; he could no longer feel his feet. He was at the end of his rope. Now Pakhom was no longer thinking about his land; he was only wondering how not to die from exhaustion.

He was afraid of dying, but he could not stop. "I have already come so far," he said, "that if I stop now, they will make fun of me!"

He heard the Baschkirs whistle and shout. At their shouts, his heart became even more stimulated than before. He summoned his last shreds of energy and continued to run. Meanwhile the sun seemed to be setting more quickly, and to be doing it on purpose. But his goal was now not too distant. Pakhom could already see the people on the hill. They signaled to him to hurry. He also saw the hat on the ground, holding the money, and the chief seated there, holding his stomach with his two hands. And Pakhom remembered his dream.

"There is a great deal of land," he thought. "God will surely permit me to live on it, will he not? No, I will not make it! I am responsible for my own failure!"

And Pakhom continued running. He looked at the sun. The sun was huge and red. It was nearing the earth; the edge was already out of sight... When Pakhom, running, arrived at the foot of the hill, the sun had set. "Oh," he thought, "everything is lost!" Now he wanted to stop, but he heard the shouts of the Baschkirs and realized that although he, at the bottom of the hill, could no longer see the sun, it was still visible to those on top of the hill. He ascended rapidly; it was still light on the hilltop. He could see the hat. The chief was seated in front of it, talking and holding his hands on his stomach.

Pakhom recalled his dream and cried: "Ah!" His knees buckled, he fell, and his hand touched the hat.

"Ah, bravo, comrade!" exclaimed the chief. "You have won a great deal of land!"

Pakhom's helper, who wanted to help him, rushed up and saw that blood was flowing from his mouth and that he was dead.

The Baschkir's tongues wagged and uttered words of regret.

The helper took the shovel and dug for Pakhom a trench just as long as his height from head to toe, three arshins, and buried him in it.

The story of Pierre, Prince of Murom

In the very center of Russia rises the city of Murom, where there formerly reigned a very pious prince by the name of Paul. But the devil, as is well known, has always hated piety, so from his point of view he had good reason to dog Paul maliciously. He decided to punish him by taking the form of a dragon and visiting Paul's spouse every day in an attempt to possess her. But while the dragon showed himself to the princess under his true colors, before her subjects he took the form of the prince himself and thus was very successful in deceiving her court.

The princess informed her spouse about what was happening to her. She had tried to resist the diabolical mischief-maker with all of her strength, but he had made fun of her puny efforts. With his satanic powers, he dominated her. The prince reflected on the situation. His dearest wish was to kill the dragon, but he simply did not know how to set about doing it. He addressed his companion:

"Wife, day and night I have reflected on how I might free you from this dragon, but I am ignorant of what might be fatal to him. Question him skilfully if you can, and try to discover what end awaits him. If you are lucky enough to obtain a response to your question and wise enough to communicate it to us, it is not only in this life that you will be freed from his noxious breath and from the evil he has made you commit, but in the afterlife as well. For our Lord and Judge Jesus Christ will reserve for you a front-row seat in the Kingdom of Heaven."

Paul's words winged their way straight to the princess' heart, and she resolved to follow his precepts faithfully. As early as the next day, when the dragon paid her a visit, she began to question him with considerable skill. She praised his great wisdom and asked him if his fund of knowledge enabled him even to foresee his own death.

The devil, that unsavory seducer, let himself be seduced in his turn by her words. Dazzled by her flattery, he revealed to the princess his most precious secret.

"I shall suffer death through the arm of Pierre and the sword Agrikos."

Although she was completely mystified by this declaration, the young woman took it to heart, imprinted it on her memory and, after the dragon had left, communicated it to her spouse.

The latter was plunged into a state of deep astonishment. He was as ignorant as she of the meaning of the arm of Pierre and the sword Agrikos. Yet he had a younger brother by the name of Pierre. A few days after that, he had him called and reported to him the words of the dragon. The young man was very impressed by these disclosures. He did not doubt that he would have a role to play in the death of the dragon and decided to kill him. However, Pierre also was bothered by a grave doubt, for he too was totally ignorant of what the sword Agrikos might be.

He was accustomed to going to church alone, and as it happened, there was one in the Convent of the Holy Cross. It was there that he directed his steps and prayed with all his heart. Then he had a vision. A boy approached and said to him: "Prince, if you wish, I will show you the sword Agrikos." Overwhelmed with enormous joy at the thought that his prayer was about to be answered, Pierre

156

asked him to show it to him. "Follow me," said the boy, and he revealed to him a fissure in the main altar. Through it they could perceive a sword.

Prince Pierre seized the weapon, rejoined his brother and waited for the propitious moment to execute his plan. Each day he went to visit his sister-in-law, and regularly found her with her husband. One day as he was leaving empty-handed one more time, he adressed the valets whom he encountered:

"There is one thing that troubles me," he said. "I have just gone from my brother's rooms to my sister-in-law's. Prince Paul did not accompany me. And yet he seemed to be present all over. I left him in his room, and he greeted me in the room of his spouse!"

"Sire," one of the valets responded, "your brother did not leave his suite."

The young prince was thoughtful as he departed, and began to have an inkling of the dragon's deception. He went directly to his older sibling's chambers and found he was indeed just where Pierre had left him.

The two brothers then agreed that Paul would not budge from his room, so that it would be impossible to make a fatal mistake, and Prince Pierre prepared to kill the devilish dragon, with the help of God.

He took hold of the sword Agrikos and went to the apartment of his sister-in-law. The dragon was there, and in his eyes appeared to be taking on the undeniable aspect of his brother. But convinced by now that he was not really looking at Paul, he smote him with a powerful saber thrust that restored the monster's original appearance. The dragon fell dead at Pierre's feet, not without having preliminarily showered him with his blood. And this impure blood began to eat away the skin of the young prince. Covered with abscesses and wounds, Pierre became gravely ill. He had the doctors of the city summoned one after the other, but none of them could alleviate his suffering.

The prince had heard it said that the doctors in the country of Ryazan were more competent than those of Murom and ordered that a trip there be arranged. He was in such bad condition that he could no longer mount a horse. They therefore transported him

to the country of Ryazan, where he sent his men to look for medical help. One of his servants took the wrong road and arrived in a village called Laskovo. Somewhat out of the way, he found a cottage that seemed deserted. He entered; there was no one to receive him. He made his way into a room and was surprised by a charming tableau: a very beautiful young girl was weaving, while a hare leaped beside her. She addressed him:

"I know that it is unusual to leave a house without ears and a room without eyes!"

The young valet could not make heads or tails of this. He asked her:

"Where is the proprietor of this place, if you please?"

"Father and Mother have gone to shed some tears, while my brother has left to gaze at death between his legs."

The young man was still at sea. He looked around him in astonishment and went on:

"I have just entered this place and surprised you as you were working, with this hare at your side, and since then you have not stopped making strange statements that I do not understand at all. You started out by saying that it is unusual to leave a house without ears and a room without eyes; then you spoke about your father and your mother, who have gone to shed some tears; and finally you mentioned a brother who left to gaze at death between his legs. And I have not the slightest notion what it is all about."

She answered him gently.

"What is so strange about it? You entered and encountered no one until you reached here. If the house had been protected by a dog who had heard you coming and barked, we could say that it had ears. If a valet had been on watch by my door, if he had seen you come in and had alerted me, we could say that this room was blessed with eyes. As to what I said concerning my father, my mother and my brother, that is not difficult to understand, either. Father and Mother have gone to a funeral, where they will undoubtedly shed some tears, as others will weep on the day when death comes in search of us. And now let me explain to you the reference to my brother. Father and he are in the honey business. They climb the trees where bees nest and gather up the precious liquid. Today, as usual, my brother is occupied with this. Each time that he reaches the top of a tree, he slowly looks between his legs toward the bottom, so as to make sure that he is safely positioned. If he fell, it would be to his death. That is why I said that he gazed at death between his legs."

"I see, young lady, that you are full of wisdom. Tell me, what is your name?"

"I am named Fevronia," she replied.

He spoke to her unreservedly.

"I am a servant of Prince Pierre of Murom. My master is afflicted with a serious illness that causes him to suffer a great deal. He has been infected by the blood of a dragon that he slew with his own hands. Until now, no doctor or other healer has been able to help him; that is why we have journeyed to your country, where the doctors have an excellent reputation. Yet we are not familiar with the names of any of them, and we do not know where to find them. Is it possible that you might inform us?"

"If the prince were willing to give himself over completely to an individual, that would suffice to bring about a cure."

Once more the valet was surprised.

"What are you saying? How could the prince give himself to anyone? The person who cures our master will be richly rewarded. Be kind and give me the name of a doctor; also, tell me where I can find him."

But she only answered:

"Bring your prince to me. If his heart is gentle and his spirit humble, he will be cured."

The valet returned to Pierre's presence and reported faithfully what he had seen and heard. The prince asked that he be brought to Fevronia. Then, changing his mind, he decided rather to send to her emissaries with this message: "Tell me, young lady, who will cure me, and you will be rewarded generously."

She responded to him in this fashion: "It is I who will cure you, and I do not desire any reward." And she added, for the sake of the servants:

"Repeat these exact words to your master: There is only one condition precedent to the cure, only one but an important one: he

must marry me."

The emissaries returned and transmitted this curious response. Prince Pierre was not angry. He simply thought: "How can a prince marry the daughter of a honey-seeker?" and decided to try to outwit her. He had this response sent to her: "Cure me if you can, and I will marry you."

Fevronia, however, was not lacking in caution. She went to look for a small receptacle, that she filled with a liquid on which she blew lightly. She handed it to the prince's men.

"First of all, prepare a bath for your master. When he is in the water, smear his body with this ointment. Rub each bump, each abcess with it except one. He will be cured."

The messengers brought back the precious liquid. The prince ordered them to prepare his bath. Overcome with curiosity and wondering if the wisdom of the young girl was really as great as his valets had reported, he decided to put her to the test. He sent her several strands of flax with this message: "If you wish, oh damsel, to become my wife as a tribute to your wisdom, prove your mettle by weaving from this flax shirt, shorts and linen with which to dry myself when I get out of the bath."

Whereupon a valet brought the few threads to Fevronia and transmitted the message to her. By way of response, she sent the servant to the woodshed with orders to bring a piece of wood back to her. The valet obeyed and brought back a log. She estimated its thickness and asked him to split it in two.

"Now," she said, "take the smaller piece and bring it to your master. Ask him to take it and carve me a weaving loom while I set up and spin the flax."

The valet brought back the wood and transmitted the message. The prince exclaimed:

"Return to the place you came from and tell the lady that it is altogether impossible to carve a weaving loom from such a small log, and in so little time!"

Upon which Fevronia delivered this response to him:

"If it is not possible, how would it be possible to weave from three strands of flax a shirt, shorts and linen, and in such a short time?"

On hearing these words faithfully repeated, the prince was

completely amazed by the wit and wisdom of the young girl.

He decided to take his bath and follow her specifications to the letter: he applied the ointment to his bumps and abscesses, one after the other, with the exception of a single one.

On leaving the bath, he found his pain had already vanished, and by the next day his body was once more smooth and healthy, save for one spot, the spot where he had failed to apply the ointment. The prince was elated over this swift cure. However, he had no intention of marrying the girl and, as compensation, showered her with valuable gifts, which she refused.

Pierre returned to his own country, and when he reached his home city of Murom, he was completely healed except for the ulcer that he had failed to rub with ointment. From that very day, however, the abscess began to spread and to give rise to others until his whole body was once more covered with them. Soon he was as ill as he had been formerly. He decided to depart again, sent his messengers to Fevronia, and once more asked for her help. She answered calmly and serenely that he would be cured only if he married her.

The prince promised solemnly. Fevronia sent him some more ointment, with the same instructions as before. The prince rapidly got well and married her.

And that is how Fevronia became a princess!

Pierre and Fevronia returned to Murom, where they lived happily, and yet never forgot the word of God.

In the meantime, Prince Paul gave his soul to heaven, and Pierre succeeded him as head of the city.

It was then that things became very complicated. The nobles did not like the princess, and their wives still less. She did not belong to their caste.

They began to complain to the prince.

"Your wife does not rise at the end of the meal, as etiquette demands; she pushes and piles together the crumbs left on the table as if she were hungry!"

Doubting his wife for a moment, the prince invited her to his table. At the end of the meal, as a matter of fact, she collected some crumbs of bread, as was her habit, and kept them in her hand.

The prince seized her wrist, ordered her to open her palm, and discovered in it frankencense and thyme! What fragrance they exuded! The prince decided that henceforth he would never doubt his companion and that he would never again put her to the test.

But the nobles were not silenced for very long. They renewed their attack and said to their prince:

"We are very happy that you rule over us with honor and dignity; we recognize you as our peerless leader and respect you, but we do not want Fevronia to be the head of our wives. If you wish to continue to reign in this country, choose another companion. Shower Fevronia with great riches and send her away."

The prince did not react with any more emotion than he showed normally; calmly and very gently he answered them:

"I suggest that you go and complain directly to the Princess Fevronia. It is she who will give you your answer."

Shaking with anger, losing all sense of decency and shame, the nobles organized a huge celebration. And there, with the temporary high spirits induced by drink and good food, without any restraint, in that akin to hunting dogs attacking their prey, they addressed the princess.

"Princess Fevronia, we are addressing you in the name of the city and the nobles and demanding that you grant us that which we ask of you."

"I will grant you what you ask on the condition that you in turn grant me a wish, one wish only," she replied.

"We are all loyal subjects of Prince Pierre, and we are content that he rules over us, but our wives resent your presence. Take everything you want and go away... anywhere your heart desires!"

She retorted:

"I have promised to accede to your wishes; it is now up to you to grant me what I ask of you."

Thinking they could guess what she wanted and being secretly convinced that everything would work out, the nobles answered:

"We will give you anything that you ask!"

"I ask nothing other than Prince Pierre, my husband," declared Fevronia.

The nobles exclaimed: "If he himself is perfectly willing to grant your wish, we shall not be disposed to oppose you." They thought to themselves that that would not inconvenience them. "When Prince Pierre is no longer here, well, we will choose someone else." And each in his heart secretly hoped that he would be the chosen one.

Yet Pierre, who had always acted in accordance with the Word of God, had no thought of not following it on this occasion, either. What did his kingdom matter compared to the Holy Scripture, and did the latter not say, in the Gospel of Matthew, that "He who casts off a spouse, except that she has committed adultery, breaks the bonds of marriage." Thus he abdicated and gave up his throne to follow Fevronia and the Word of God. The nobles accompanied them as far as the Oka River, that flowed at the base of the city walls and where they prepared to embark.

At nightfall the travelers halted on the shore of the river. Pierre was beset by troublesome thoughts, not knowing how they were going to live. However, Fevronia had not lost confidence.

"Do not worry, my prince," she said. "God our Creator will aid us in our need. Have faith; He will not abandon us."

On the shore refreshments were being prepared for them. The cook hung his pots and utensils on a nearby bush. Seeing this, the princess blessed the shrub and said to it: "Take the trouble to grow until tomorrow; in one night become a strong and powerful tree, with branches and thick foliage, and thus delay our departure."

However, the next day all preparations were quickly made. The boat was reloaded, and they were about to continue their odyssey when emissaries arrived from Murom and declared:

"Oh, Prince, the whole city has sent us after you to beg you not to desert us, poor orphans, and to retrace your steps. Many people have died this night. Wanting to take your place, numerous nobles have slain one another. But those who are still alive, as well as all of your subjects, beseech you humbly. We know that we disappointed you by asking you to repudiate the Princess Fevronia because of our wives. We beg you to pardon us. Do not abandon us. Come back; your slaves ask it on their knees."

Therefore Pierre and Fevronia returned to Murom and continued to reign, faithfully obeying the Word of God, praying regularly and devoting themselves to the accomplishment of good deeds.

They became a father and a mother to all of their subjects, loving all of them equally.

When they had a premonition that their end was approaching, they asked God to take them at the same time and had a sarcophagus made in which they could be interred next to one another. They chose the stone and asked that they be separated from one another only by a thin partition.

Finally they retired into convents where they pronounced their vows. Prince Pierre became Brother David, and Fevronia took the name of Euphrosine.

The holy princess then began to embroider with her own hands an altar cloth destined for the Cathedral. On it she reproduced with great skill the portraits of numerous saints. It was then that she received a first message from the prince. He said to her: "Sister Euphrosine, I feel the moment approaching when my soul is going to leave my body; do not forget that together we both made the vow that we would be together in the kingdom of God."

"Wait a little longer, my Lord; I have not had the time to finish my work." Shortly afterward he sent her a second message. "I cannot wait very much longer," and finally a third: "My soul is soaring aloft; it waits for yours!"

Fevronia had had the time to finish her altar cloth. The face of the last saint was embroidered; all that was lacking were a few stitches on her habit. She posed her needle there and sent a response by the same messenger. "It is time, my friend; let us die together." She withdrew to pray and peacefully yielded up her soul to God on the twenty-fifth day of the month of June.

After their deaths, and in spite of the wishes of the two spouses, the people decided that Prince Pierre would be buried in Saint Mary's Cathedral, while the remains of the princess would remain outside the walls, in the church of the Convent of the Holy Cross.

The nobles held a meeting. "It would not be at all proper for two persons of opposite sexes, who had pronounced their vows and lived like saints, to be buried in the same sarcophagus."

Thus they had two new tombs built and buried the bodies in them. As to the sarcophagus that Pierre and Fevronia had had carved from a single stone, they placed it, empty, in the cathedral where the remains of the prince rested.

The day after this ill-considered act, they found their tombs empty, while the two bodies reposed side by side in the coffin constructed as a refuge for their corpses. Their subjects, the same subjects who had tormented them during their lives and who were so lacking in both wisdom and respect, continued to persecute them even beyond the grave. On several occasions they replaced each of them in an individual tomb, only to find them united anew the next morning. This went on until they finally understood that God Himself had chosen Saint Mary's Cathedral to be the resting place of the two spouses; the holy ornaments still have the power, even today, to heal those who who approach them with faith in their hearts.

The young girl
and the moon

Once upon a time, in the country of Tchuktuchen, there lived an old man whose daughter was his sole support. However, he saw her only rarely. In the summer, she looked after the flocks one hour away from the camp where he resided, and in the winter she went off a still greater distance with their livestock. She returned to the house with her team only when she needed supplies.

One night one of her reindeer lifted his head toward the heavens, contemplated the sky for a moment and said to her:

"Look! Oh, look!"

She raised her eyes in turn and saw the prince, The Moon, descend from the sky in a sled drawn by reindeer.

"Where can he be going?" asked the girl. "What is he looking for?"

"It is you he is looking for," the reindeer replied. "He is coming to kidnap you!"

The girl began to tremble with fear.

"What can I do to escape from him?"

The reindeer started to dig a hole in the snow with his hoofs.

"Hide quickly in this," he said.

She obeyed him, and he covered over the spot with snow. She was completely concealed when the prince The Moon set foot on the ground. He began to search, after fastening his animals, very thoroughly and carefully. He could not find her. Yet he passed very close to the little knoll under which she lay, but saw nothing out of the ordinary there. "How is it possible?" exclaimed The Moon. "Where can she possibly have disappeared? I am going to go up to my home again, but I will return without warning. And the next time I will find her, the beauty, and I will take her away with me!" He settled himself on his sled and disappeared in the heavens.

"He has left," said the reindeer, and he rapidly uncovered the girl with the help of his muzzle. "Let us go the camp at once, for he will come back. We will be able to hide better there."

She seated herself on her sled, and the reindeer carried her off as quickly as he could. Arriving at the camp, she ran to her father's tent. He was not there. Who else might be able to help her?

"Hurry and hide," the reindeer said to her. "We risk being discovered by him!"

"But where do you suggest I hide?"

"Don't be concerned, for I am going to change you into a... What about changing you into a billy goat?"

"He'll be sure to guess," said the girl, tears in her eyes.

"And if I changed you into a hammer?"

"He would still guess!"

"And if I changed you ... into a tent pole?"

"He'd guess anyway!"

"And if I transformed you into a thread in the carpet?"

"He would find me nevertheless; he would be sure to know!"

"In that case, what do you want me to do? Perhaps change you into an oil lamp?"

"Oh, yes, yes, that's exactly what I need."

"Sit down there," said the reindeer, and he began to rub his hoofs against the earth. And the girl was changed into a lamp and began to burn, illuminating the whole tent with her light.

During this time, the prince The Moon had once more descended to earth and was seeking her among her animals. Since she was not there, he made his way to the camp. He fastened his reindeer and entered the tent. He examined each stake and each utensil, one by one, looked under the beds, patted the hides of the animals, ransacked everything systematically. Nothing afforded a clue.

He did not notice the lamp, for it shone with a brilliance similar to his.

"Strange, strange," said The Moon. "Where might she well be? Will I have to depart empty-handed once more?" He left the tent and unfastened his reindeer. He was getting ready to leave when he perceived the face of the girl. She had half-opened the matting that served to close the tent and was laughing.

"I am here, and you cannot catch me!" she called.

The prince The Moon jumped from his sled and ran into the tent. The girl had just enough time to take the form of a lamp again. He commenced his search anew, in desperation. Not a speck of dust escaped him, not a crumb under the table. He even pawed through the straw mattresses. All without result. "Where in the world can she be? Will I have to go away empty-handed once more?"

He had barely seated himself on his sled when the tent again opened a crack, and she appeared revealed from the waist up. Laughing again, she called to him:

"I am there, and you cannot catch me!"

The Moon rushed under the tent and searched for her one last time. He put everything topsy-turvy, upset the furniture, scoured the premises until he was exhausted.

Feebly he went out of the tent; his legs were barely able to carry him as far as his sled. Then the girl lost all fear. Taking on her true form, she ran out of the tent, jumped on the back of The Moon and immobilized his wrists and ankles.

"Oh," exclaimed The Moon, "you want my life! Very well, kill me! It will be my own fault, because I wished to carry you away against your will. But before you cause my death, fulfill one last wish of mine. Take me into your tent for a while to warm me. I am so cold..."

The girl was amazed.

"How can you be cold, you who have neither tent nor a roof over your head. You are always out of doors, and it is there you will remain."

The prince The Moon renewed his pleas.

"Do not be so cruel; give me my freedom. It is true that I have neither hearth nor home. I am a vagabond. But if you will be kind enough to release me, I will repay you a thousand times over, and all of your people will have reason to rejoice. I will give you nights as bright as day... I will measure the year.... I will change each month. You will see. First will come the month of the bull, then that of the calf; the month of the great waters, then that of the leaves; the month of heat, followed by that when our animals change their horns; the month when reindeer mate, and the first month of winter..."

"If I release you and you regain your strength, will you not once more want to kidnap me?"

"Oh, no, never again! You are too clever for me! I will re-ascend to the vault of the sky. Give me my freedom, I beg of you, so that I may give you light!"

The girl gave him his freedom, and it is as a token of his gratitude that The Moon, to this very day, sends his white light onto the earth.

The miraculous flower

In the country about which we are speaking, the sun shone during the day and the moon at night. The earth was fertile, the wheat fine and abundant. In addition to a good climate, the land possessed a people who were good workers. They toiled all day and sometimes until late at night. Was it for that reason they were in such bad humor? They spent all their time becoming angry with one another and arguing, and never wished one another well! And as they were large and strong, as well as disputatious, they frequently came to blows. It even happened that sometimes one of the combatants finished the struggle wet with his own blood, without the strength to get up, while the other returned to his home with his head hanging even lower than usual. Laughter and joy had disappeared from the country. Impossible to be happy in a place where love was dead, impossible in spite of all its riches.

Yet there was one person who was extremely affectionate and who smiled at everyone. It was Akulina, the daughter of the old Ivan Gregorovitch. The latter was esteemed by everyone and genuinely respected because of his wisdom and his kindness. Akulina was very beautiful. She possessed a magnificent head of dark hair, into which in the morning she stuck various flowers whose perfume remained with her throughout the day. When she walked in the garden, a fawn gamboled at her side, and the birds descended from the trees to greet her.

Beyond the large river that was the country's northern frontier began the realm of that malevolent creature who was prince of ice. His lands were of a dazzling whiteness for as far as the eye could see. A cold wind blew day and night, and enormous icicles hung from the trees and the rocks. The prince lived in a glass palace (or was it not rather, once again, simply made of ice?), where one never heard a human voice, where no man had ever entered, where the only living creatures were the elves and gnomes in the service of the prince. They glided noiselessly across the rooms of the palace.

The prince spent most of his time cosily snuggled in his kingdom. Yet it sometimes came to pass that he crossed the frontier river and strolled in the country of the sun in a halo of snowflakes. Everyone hid when he approached; animals went into their holes. They feared him as if he were the plague.

Nevertheless, the inhabitants of the country about which we are speaking one day decided to oppose him. They were not lacking in courage. However, when there was a question of designating the person who would attack him first, quarrels and arguments broke out afresh and even resulted in several deaths. That is why they abandoned any idea of resisting. The prince retained all of his power, and they their anxiety and fear.

One day, unfortunately, the prince of ice heard about the beautiful young woman whose dark hair was entwined with flowers. It also heard it said that she had magnificent blue eyes, a charming voice, and a merry laugh that was captivating. "She is just what I need," he thought, for he had grown weary of his solitude.

He set forth, surrounded as usual by many snowflakes, and flew to the country of radiant sun. His presence alone was enough to cover everything with a white powder. The sun shrank with displeasure. Very quickly he reached the house of Ivan Gregorovitch, that was located on a small hill, surrounded by high pines. He wore a brilliant white suit, and on his back two black wings glittered. His features were somber and cruel, his gaze icy.

Ivan Gregorovitch was seated in his old easy chair, with Akulina at his side. Nestling against one another, they watched with terror as the prince of ice stood near the door and looked down on them. The oldster finally asked him what he wanted.

"I have come to take your daughter as my wife," answered the prince with a grimace.

"My daughter?" exclaimed Ivan Gregorovitch despairingly. "She will never be yours!"

"If you refuse to give her to me, I will take her by force," responded the prince of ice, and each word that fell from his lips was like a ball of ice.

Akulina answered him in her turn. She had regained her poise and was calm.

"I will never be your wife, Prince, never, absolutely never. Moreover, you cannot take me away against my will, for you know as well as I that all of the forces of good will unite to protect me. Neither are you ignorant of the fact that their strength is superior to yours. Therefore I beseech you to return to the place whence you came."

At these words, the prince had become even more pale, if that were possible. Yet his eyes shone with a diabolical light.

"You are right; I confess it, "he said. "I cannot take you by force. But do not congratulate yourself prematurely, for I am going to transform you into a cake of ice. The life will go out of you! And after you, it will be your entire country that will suffer. I am going to cover everything with hoar frost, and gradually all life will be extinguished. Only love will be able to save you, but how do you expect it to penetrate a thick coating of frost?"

He stretched out his arms, blew on the young woman with his icy breath and disappeared.

Akulina collapsed in her father's arms, her limbs stiffened, and life appeared to leave her body.

Shouting loudly, Ivan Gregorovitch called to his servants. The house was filled with lamentations. They carried Akulina to her bed, just beside the stove. They lighted candles.

Her father could not bring himself to leave his daughter. And even

the old healer, who was usually so effective, seemed to be all at sea. She wrang her hands in anguish, while Ivan Gregorovitch wept.

A thick layer of snow and covered the whole country. Flowers hung sadly on their stems before they froze; the trees lost their leaves. The water of the brooks turned to ice; rivers and lakes, everything was soon frozen into silence. And the weeks passed. The sun refused to shine; the country was immersed in a cold obscurity in which tears and groans mingled.

Food began to be in short supply; wood became rare; people were barely able to keep warm. Illness ran rampant. But surely the saddest development was that Akulina seemed dead and that her heart, the only one that apparently had held love for all, had ceased to beat. The populace scrutinized one another even more darkly than before; all joy and all light had vanished from their eyes.

Yet one cottage, just on the edge of the forest, still contained a little warmth and joy; it was the only one. It sheltered a young man and his mother. The fire in his chimney had not been extinguished, for Aliosha went into the forest almost every day to search for wood. He and his mother had succeeded in avoiding hunger, and in spite of the absence of the sun, joy and hope had not completely abandoned them, for they loved one another. And they were warmed by this love.

Aliosha was hard-working and skillful. One day when he went to the village, he heard people complaining bitterly, threw them a word of encouragement and nodded his head before departing. On returning to his home, he once more went into the forest to look for wood.

It had snowed during the night, and the branches of the trees were heavy with its weight. The air was icy and still. Soon Aliocha had filled his basket. He sat down on a tree trunk for a moment. Just at that instant a dwarf, gray from head to foot, appeared before him. Big tears were running down his furrowed cheeks.

"Hello," Aliosha said to him. "What are you doing here, my good man, and why are you crying like that?"

"Oh, oh!" was the dwarf's only response, and he drew from his pocket a handkerchief of fine batiste. "A great misfortune has overtaken us, and all because of the famous white prince! We poor dwarves hardly dare any longer slip into our subterranean realm.

175

The earth is as hard as stone, and if this situation lasts for very much longer, we are all going to die of cold."

His sobs evoked deep pity in Aliosha.

"For us humans," he said to him, "the situation is equally unbearable."

The dwarf conceded this. Aliosha was filled with sadness as he returned home. However, when he saw the fire blazing merrily, his depression melted like snow in the sun, and he quickly forgot the unhappiness of the dwarf.

The next day, he left early to look under the snow for grass for his goat. He collected a brimming basketful, then sat down for a minute at the foot of a solitary tree and let his gaze wander over the surrounding whiteness. A murmur of wings interrupted his reverie. A large bird had just alit on the snow, in front of him. His eyes were shadowed by infinite sadness. He began his croaking complaint: "Poor birds that we are, we will soon no longer have anything to eat. The snow is rising higher and higher, and the icy air is paralyzing our wings." He moved his wings with difficulty, while huge tears flowed over his plumage.

Aliosha did not know how to answer him. Why did they all come like this to complain to him? He retraced his footsteps, his heart heavy.

Soon afterward his mother asked him:

"Aliosha, my beloved child, soon we will be completely out of water; won't you please go to look for some on the bank of the river?"

He took an axe and two pails and went down to the river. He made a hole in the ice so he could draw out water. The coat of ice was thick, and he had to make several attempts. And when finally he was about to throw in his pail, a fish showed its head in the opening. He began by taking a deep breath, then addressed Aliosha:

"Oh me, I was afraid; I thought I was not going to find a simple air bubble! Things are not going too well for us, the inhabitants of the river; if this continues, we will all be wiped out! If only someone were willing to give us some help!"

"Yes," replied Aliosha, "if only someone were willing to give us some help... Oh, if only I could do something about it, I would

willingly do it."

Hardly had he spoken these words when he heard the beating of wings, and the big bird landed on the ice in front of him. "You can do something!" he croaked. "You can!" repeated the fish. "You can!" finally said a voice behind him. He turned around and perceived the dwarf.

Aliosha could not believe his ears. He sat down on a rock and asked:

"How can I help you, I who have so little intelligence?"

"You can," the tree replied in chorus.

"But how?"

It was then that the dwarf approached him. He murmured in his ear in a voice pregnant with mystery: "Go in search of the miraculous flower." "It is now a long time since the white prince stole it from us, and if you bring it back, there will be nothing left him to do but to go back home and cede his place in the sun," added the fish. And the bird croaked: "If you bring it back to us, you will deliver us all, men and animals, from the cold!"

Aliosha did not know what to think. "But where will I find it?" he inquired.

"In the kingdom of the white prince," replied the fish, while the bird and the dwarf nodded agreement with their heads. "Tell me more about it," asked Aliosha. And the dwarf began his recital.

"On the other side of the river, very far from here, in the very heart of the deserted and depressing country that belongs to the prince of ice, there rises a huge tower that is guarded by three ferocious beasts: a wolf, an owl, and a white bear. All three are strong and determined, and only a man endowed with extreme valor can vanquish their strong will. This tower houses only a single room, and it is there that you will find the miraculous flower, enclosed in a glass chest. She spends her time weeping, she is so homesick for our land of sun. Know one thing: she has been imprisoned there for a very long time indeed, and with her all joy in the country vanished in thin air. For it is she who caused the hearts of men to rejoice, who gave them a sense of beauty and goodness. As long as she was here, everything went well for us. Laughter was our companion. People smiled, helped one another and understood one another, for they loved one another. And then misfortune struck. The prince of ice came, in the middle of a storm, and snatched her from he meadow, put her in a glass chest and carried her away. As soon as she disappeared, all mercy and kidness seemed to quit men's hearts, giving way to envy and, worse, to jealousy. They had ceased loving one another. However, we have not forgotten it, any more than we have forgotten our poor Akulina. And since your heart is pure, you are the only one who can help us free her."

"Of course I will go in search of her," promised Aliosha, filled with enthusiasm. "I will set her free, no matter what it costs me!"

"We will all be grateful to you," croaked the bird, "for we are already closer to death than to life."

The fish, who had not ceased swallowing air, exclaimed:

"You must undoubtedly free our poor beautiful Akulina. It will be enough if you bring her the flower; her eyes will open, and she will come back to life."

"I will do what I can very willingly," declared Aliosha.

He rose and took his pail, ready to leave, but the dwarf detained him. "If you need any help, do not hesitate to call on us. It will be enough to strike the ground three times and call:

"Dwarf friends, come here!"
and all of my brothers will come to your aid."

The bird approached with a swish of his wings and said to him:
"And if it is our help that you need, don't hesitate in that case either. It will be enough to call:

"Bird friends, come here!"
and all of my brothers will come to your aid."

And the fish added: "It is not impossible that you might also have need of us. In that case, do not hesitate to call:

"Fish-friends, come here!"
and all of my brothers will swim to your aid."

Aliosha thanked them from the bottom of his heart and promised that he would not rest until he had liberated the miraculous flower. After which he filled his pails and returned home.

As early as the next day he set forth. Fearful and trembling, his mother watched him move off. "If only he can succeed," she thought, and wished him well with all her heart. First Aliosha directed his steps to the house of Ivan Gregorovitch. He wanted to see Akulina and, above all, to console her father, for he had heard it said everywhere that his grief was boundless. He was greeted by silence in the dwelling. The servants glided on their soft slippers and whispered to each other the orders of the master. The dogs themselves had slunk into corners, their tails between their legs. The old healer led Aliosha into Akulina's room. As always, Ivan Gregorovitch was seated at the bedside of his daughter, and the deep sorrow with which his heart was burdened had turned his hair white.

"It seems that you wish to help us," he said to Aliosha.

"Certainly I will help all of you, and first of all Akulina."

"If you bring my daughter back to life, she will be yours, and also my house, that you will inherit after my death."

Aliosha, very grateful, bowed before Ivan Gregorovitch, kissed Akulina's icy hand and went on his way.

Many days advancing on foot separated him from the great river. Everywhere he encountered misery and hunger. And everywhere there was also hatred, and it was that which saddened him the most, the hatred that set men against one another. Each time he observed it his heart grew heavier, and he passed by his peers without stopping, more eager than ever to reach his goal. When he finally perceived the great river, he immediately realized that it was the first serious obstacle he had encountered. He began to reflect. Impossible to cross it by swimming; the water was too cold and the current too strong. "Am I already to be forced to stop here?" he wondered, perplexed. "Never in the world!" he exclaimed, and suddenly remembered the words of the fish. Putting his hands in front of his mouth like a megaphone, he called:

"Fish friends, come here!"

The water appeared to shiver, and at the same instant a band of fish shone in front of him. One of them, imposing in size, wore a crown on his head. He addressed Aliosha:

"You called us; what is it you need?"

"Help me cross the river!"

"Place your feet on us, and you will see what happens," the fish advised.

In a flash he was on the other side of the river, without a single drop of water having wet his shoes.

Aliosha thanked the fish and continued on his journey. He was now treading on enemy territory. Once again he had to walk for many days and many nights in snow and on ice. There was not a single living creature to speak to; only an occasional tree, stunted and stripped bare, the sight of which inspired in him more fear than pleasure. For the black silhouettes evoked sinister phantoms. Finally he saw something like a dark bar on the horizon. When he was nearer, Aliosha perceived that he was standing in front of a deep ravine. "How can I cross it?" he said to himself, and was preparing to descend the steep slope when he recalled the words of the bird. Once more using his hands, he called as loudly as he could:

"Bird friends, come here!"

And the sky, deserted until then, was suddenly filled with birds. An eagle alit alongside him and said to him:

"What do you need?"

"I have to cross this ravine," said Aliosha.

And before he could say anything more, he found himself in the air, and soon was on the other side of the ravine, where they put him down gently. "Thank you, my friends," he called, and continued on his way, while the birds took off in another direction.

Three days and three nights later, he finally reached the tower which the dwarf had told him about. It was surrounded by a wall that was as high as it was slippery, and in spite of all his efforts, Aliosha could not succeed in scaling it. It was then that he thought of the little gray, wrinkled, appealing creature. He struck the ground three times and called:

"Dwarf friends, come here!"

Suddenly a hole opened at his feet. It led to a gallery. Aliosha observed a midget who signaled to follow him. He entered the tunnel and followed his guide to a brilliantly lighted room. A throng of elves was assembled there around their king. The latter addressed Aliosha from his throne.

"What do you need?"

Aliosha bowed and replied:

"I have come to liberate the miraculous flower, and I ask your

180

help so that I can reach the tower."

"Your aim is a noble one, and you can count on us," answered the king. "Moreover, how can I express to you to what extent we pity that flower. We can hear her weep from here, and each time it touches our hearts. However, you will need a great deal of courage, for the beasts that guard her are cruel."

"I feel myself armed with incredible courage," replied Aliosha, "if only you will help me to get inside the tower."

The king rose and personally conducted him to the entrance to a new gallery.

"Follow this corridor," he said. "It will lead you to the courtyard that separates the tower from the surrounding wall. It is there, just before the exit, that my dwarves will wait for you."

Aliocha thanked the little king and hastened to the corridor. When he went out into the fresh air, he was at the foot of the tower.

The wolf, lying in front of the entrance, must have been asleep, for he stretched. Hardly had he caught sight of Aliosha, however, when he opened his eyes wide, howled and rushed at him. But the young man dealt him such a savage blow on the muzzle with his fists that he fell over backwards, as if dead.

Aliosha was cautiously approaching the tower when an enormous owl came out of it with a terrible beating of his wings. His eyes were red and glittered like live charcoal. His claws extended, he propelled himself toward Aliosha.

The latter, fortunately in control of himself, seized the bird by its claws and hurled it against the wall with such force that it fell unconscious.

It was then that Aliosha saw the bear coming. This time his heart froze. The animal stared at him with his little black eyes, that had an evil glare. What should he do now? A blow with his fist would certainly be totally ineffective. Aliosha noticed a stone to his left. He promptly grabbed it and threw it as hard as he could at the very moment the beast was about to seize him. The projectile hit the white bear in the head, and he fell to the ground.

At last Aliosha could enter into the tower. A spiral staircase led to the one room it contained. He was welcomed by a marvelous red shimmering light and by a perfume unlike any other. On a glass pedestal, he perceived the chest in which the flower was enclosed. The light that entered there played on the glass partitions, that sent back purple sparks. The spectacle was so impressive that Aliosha stood still for a moment, paralyzed by the sight of so much beauty.

Finally, very gently he took hold of the glass chest and made his way to the stairs. The bear, the owl and the wolf had not yet regained consciousness. Aliosha crossed the courtyard and hastened to the subterranean passage where the dwarves awaited him.

It was only when he arrived there that he became aware of just how fast his heart was beating. The elves led him back to their king. "You are good and courageous," the latter told him. "But I do not want to delay you; return home as quickly as possible, for the white prince will lose no time finding out what you have done, and he will try to overtake you. Take care of yourself!"

Aliosha departed. The fear that the prince of ice might recapture the flower gave wings to his feet. He felt no fatigue. For days and nights he covered the course previously taken, going in the opposite direction, turning around from time to time to see if he was not being pursued. Finally he came within sight of the river. He was going to utter a joyful cry when he heard a commotion in the distance. He recognized the prince by the cloud of snow that accompanied him. He had only the time to press the chest against his heart and to speed up his pace still further. Arriving at the water's edge, he called out the magic words and jumped on the backs of the fish that arrived.

Having been once more deposited, completely dry, on the far shore, Aliosha turned around and saw the prince on the other side. His eyes in his fury were like flashes of lightning. But Aliosha felt a deep sense of peace, for he knew that he no longer had anything to fear. "Your pursuit is at an end," he called, and favored his enemy with a gesture of his hand before going on. The prince was frothing with rage; there was nothing left for him to do but to return alone to his icy realm.

Aliosha no longer needed to run. Happy, his heart finally at rest, he crossed his country in the direction of the house on the hill. Everywhere he passed, the snow and ice melted. The grass regained its former color; the flowers straightened up. People came out of their icy dwellings and, filled with astonishment, gazed at a sky that was blue again. The sun warmed them, and birds filled the air with their chirping. People cautiously began to exchange a few words, then timid smiles. At the same time the hatred in their hearts and looks was dissipated. All of them hastened toward the miraculous flower in order to look at the object that had restored love to the country.

At the home of Ivan Gregorovitch, Aliosha was welcomed with cries of joy! The old man clasped him in his arms and led him to his daughter. Hardly had the shimmering red light illuminated Akulina's pale face before she seemed to come back to life. The young woman opened her eyes almost at once.

The wedding of Aliosha and Akulina was a splendid one. The whole country joined in the celebration. As for the mother of the young man, she shed tears of joy.

For the flower, they chose the most beautiful meadow in the vicinity and decided to protect it day and night from any danger, for everyone recognized that it was impossible to live without it, since it was the source of all life, all joy and all light.

Legend of the old bell-ringer

It was dark.

The little village nestled on the shore of a river that flowed peaceably in the spring night, snuggled in the shadow of a great woods. The sky was spangled with stars. A light mist rose from ground barely awakened from its long winter sleep; it accentuated the shadows of the pines and gave a silvery hue to the water... A deep silence and a tranquillity touched with nostalgia enveloped everything... The villagers were still sleeping... The shapes of the houses could barely be discerned.

From time to time a light glittered, a door creaked, a dog barked, and then the enchanted silence of the spring night took over once more. And then people woke up... A solitary traveler came out of the woods, a horseman passed, a wagon with creaking wheels crossed the street. The inhabitants of the village made their way to church so as to begin this Easter Saturday properly.

On a hill in the center of the village a small church stood. The first glimmers of the day were reflected in its windows, whereas the steeple of gray stone was still enveloped in fog. Its stairway creaked under the uncertain steps of the old bell-ringer. In his hand he held a lantern whose light would soon merge with that of the stars.

The stairs were decidedly very steep for the old man. His feet obeyed his will with difficulty... Life had indeed tried him; moreover, his vision was poor... It was time for death to arrive, but it was making him wait. The old man had seen his sons and his grand-children perish; he had accompanied them, one by one, to their last resting place. Death had knocked everywhere save at his door; it seemed to have forgotten him. Life was becoming more and more burdensome.

His bells had often announced the Easter season. He did not even know any longer how many times he had waited there, at the top of the steeple, for the hour of the resurrection. Today again, as in the past, for it was the will of God.

The old man painfully arrived at the decrepit railing of the tower. He leaned against it; in front of him was the cemetery.

With his bad eyes he made out the regular shapes of the tomb-stones. The open arms of the crosses seemed to be protecting the dead. A few birch trees shivered; their white trunks glimmered in the half-light.

The fresh odor of buds perfumed the air, heralding the springtime. Old Micheitch filled his lungs with it, letting himself he lulled by the peace around him... What would the coming year bring him? Where would he be in twelve months: there on the heights awaiting Easter so he could announce it by ringing his bells or ... down below, under the earth? Where would they dig his grave? In that isolated corner as he wished? Would his, too, be adorned with a cross? Let the will of God be done ... he felt he was ready. But it was time to announce the sunrise. It was Holy Saturday, sublime Saturday. "Let God be honored and thanked a thousand times," his lips murmured. He lifted his eyes toward the heavens, and millions of stars saluted him. He made the sign of the cross...

"Micheitch." The old sacristan was calling to him from below. His voice was as quavering as the bell-ringer's. His eyes no longer saw too clearly, either, even though he shaded them with his hand.

They were moist with emotion.

"What do you want?" the bell-ringer replied. "I am here!" He leaned over the railing. "Here. Can't you see me, then?"

"No. Isn't it time to ring the bells? What do you think?"

Both raised their eyes toward the stars, toward the hundreds of stars that looked down on them from above; the Big Dipper shone brilliantly.

Micheitch reflected for a moment.

"It is not yet quite time," he said. "I will be well aware when the time comes."

Certainly he would be well aware; no need of a watch for that. The stars that God had made would inform him. He had never missed the hour.

Like the sky and the white cloud that stretched out yonder, the earth, and the dark pine forest that the wind caused to murmur and to sing, and the splashing of the river, invisible at that hour, all of these things were as dear to him as they were familiar. His whole life was linked to them. The past came to life again: he relived the moment when he had mounted the tower for the first time, his tiny hand in his father's... How long ago it was ... and yet how near it seemed! He saw himself as a boy; he again saw his blond curls, his brilliant eyes, and felt the wind anew, not the wind that raised the dust of the road but a very special wind, that rose higher, that caressed everything it touched, that tangled his curls... Oh, if that wind could only carry him away ... he would see the villagers become very tiny and the houses shrink before his eyes ... even the forest would look like a miniature, and he would be able to encompass the entire village at a single glance...

But our bell-ringer came back to earth. He was not so high as the clouds, but only at the height of the steeple.

The same was true of life. When one was young, it seemed long, interminable, and then it shrank. When one was old, it seemed as if it could be held in the palm of one's hand, from birth to the grave, to that grave in the corner of the cemetery for which he yearned... God be thanked, the end was near! It was as an honest man that he had traveled his hard road. The damp earth would be like a second mother for him. And if God willed, it would not be long before he reposed in its bosom.

But it was time to be busy with the bells! Micheitch cast a last glance at the stars, uncovered himself, made the sign of the cross and seized his small ropes.

At once a first peal echoed in the transparent air ... then a second, a third, a fourth ... sometimes sharp, sometimes soft and gentle... Nor did they stop completely until the start of the religious service.

When he was younger, Micheitch rapidly descended the stairs and crept into a corner of the church in order to participate in the liturgy and pray with the others. Now, however, he remained up above. His legs were too heavy; today they were heavier than ever. He let himself fall onto a bench and, his ears still ringing from the sound of the bells, surrendered to the lure of dreams. Where could they lead? No matter. The day had not yet dawned, and the principal source of light was still his lantern. It was with difficulty he could even distinguish the outlines of the tower. The muffled sound of hymns rose from the church, and the wind gently stirred the cords fastened to the iron clappers.

Micheitch let his head hang on his chest, while images from his life passed through his mind... The hymns caused his thoughts to revert to the interior of the church... Since time immemorial, youthful and mature voices had mingled, supported, united, dominated by the voice of the priest. He recalled old Father Naum. Before his eyes paraded hundreds of peasants, whose heads bowed and then were raised, whose hands made the sign of the cross... Hundreds of familiar faces, that today had disappeared... The face of his father with the stern expression and the face of his older brother, who sighed so often, and finally his own: a face in which were reflected health, youth and vigor, a face full of yearnings and hopes of happiness, full of plans for the future.

And what had become of this happiness? The thoughts of the old man burned brightly, like a dying fire on which one blows and lighted up the most secret recesses of his life, that already belonged to the past... Numerous ordeals, suffering and worry instead of happiness. Fate had assailed this man and had furrowed his face at an early age, had quickly bent his back, formerly so erect; he had soon acquired the habit of sighing as much as his elder brother...

And there to the left, in the midst of the village women, was it not his own wife he perceived? Her head bent, she was praying, in devout meditation. She had been a good wife to him, a faithful companion. God had summoned her to His care. She had had her share of trouble. Grief and hard work had aged her prematurely. Her eyes quickly lost their luster, and the pride that had been a natural attribute of a beautiful young woman had been undermined by the fear and anguish that each blow of fate renewed. She had not known happiness, either. A single one of their children had survived, a son in whom they had placed all their hopes, but his life, too, had been ruined by the wickedness and deceitfulness of men.

For in the village there was a rich usurer, who during the service knelt until his body touched the ground. He even kissed the floor tiles of the church, making expansive signs of the cross, said a hypocritical prayer for the orphans by whom he profited, and threw powder in the Lord's eyes, hoping to deceive God as he had deceived men...

Micheitch could not look at him without a pang in his heart and a feeling of distaste; and the divine images seemed to gaze at him sternly from the tops of the walls, irritated by his lying and miserable behavior... All that was behind him, long since behind him... His life today unfolded only at the summit of the tower, where the wind blew and played across the little ropes attached to the bells. "God will judge; it is to Him that vengeance belongs!" murmured the old man, while huge tears ran down his cheeks furrowed by wrinkles...

"Eh, Micheitch, you have let yourself be overcome by sleepiness!" called a voice down below. "Who is calling me?" demanded the old man, and he jumped to his feet. "My God, is it really possible?" he thought, very ashamed. He immediately seized the ropes and cast a glance toward the area below. Peasants were now surrounding the church... They resembled insects and the square looked like an ant hill.

Micheitch had slept for a long time. He saw a procession form, with crosses and sacred icons at the head; it turned around the corner of the church. "Christ is risen," shoted a joyful voice, and this shout echoed strongly in the worn-out heart of the old man...

It seemed to him that the tapers that had been brought out of the church shone more brightly than usual, and that the peasants were displaying an unaccustomed joy... He rang with all of his strength, and the wind, also awakened from its sleep, caught the sounds in midair and sent them into the atmosphere. Then the echo hurled them back, and the sky was filled with sound...

Never before had the old bell-ringer carilloned in that way. It seemed as if the fullness of his heart was finally causing it to overflow and giving life to the metal, that appeared not only to be singing as it always did, but to laugh and to cry, to explode with joy and to quiver with sadness. The stars shone and the sound soared upward to join them, filled with love and plenitude... And the great bell, most especially, seemed to repeat eternally that "the Son of God is risen!" The two others, less sonorous but not in any way shrill, sang to whoever would listen that "the Son Of God is risen!" And finally the smallest, that pealed more quickly than the others, interpolated with unexpected gaiety that "the Son of God is risen!"

And the whole bell tower seemed to share the joy of men, and the wind in person that caressed the old man's face ... all of them and everything sang and joyously proclaimed that "the Son of God is risen!"

Micheitch at last felt that his heart was relieved of all anguish, of all pain, of all worry... He finally forgot that his life and his hopes of happiness had been but empty and a dream; he no longer remembered that he was alone in the world... The sounds that resounded around him, that rose and fell from the earth to the sky and from the sky to the earth, that sang and wept, that laughed and exploded, assembled around him his children and grandchildren. He once again heard their joyful voices, that merged with the sounds of the bells, harmonized with them and were lost in them. They finally blessed him with the intense joy that he had always been refused... The bell-ringer eagerly pulled on his ropes, tears streaming down his withered cheeks; his heart, drunk with joy, beat wildly...

In the square, faces turned toward the steeple. Never, never in all the years, had the old bell-ringer carilloned so well! And then, after a pull more violent than the others, all became quiet. The smallest bell emitted something like a shrill cry, a false note, then stopped abruptly. Only the deepest bell still vibrated for an instant, sent forth a last lament and died...

And the body of the old man toppled over gently on the bench, while two last tears crossed cheeks already white... Make way! Stand back! The old bell-ringer has finished ringing!

The two blind men

In Moscow, a city built of pale stone, there lived a young man who worked by the day. One summer day he became homesick and wanted to return to his village, to rejoin his family and help them gather in the harvest. He went in search of his employer and asked that he pay him what was owed him and allow him to leave.

"Stay until the fall," the employer responded.

But the boy insisted:

"Let me return to my village."

So his employer paid him his wages, but in order to revenge himself, he made all sorts of deductions and arranged things in such a way that in the end the young man received a total of only half a ruble. He took the money, slipped a bit of bread into his pocket, fastened his felt slippers on his back and left Moscow by the highway.

When he arrived near a barrier, he saw there a blind beggar seated on a pile of stones and asking for alms. "Christians, good people, give alms to a poor blind man!"

The boy took pity on him, approached the beggar and gave him the half-ruble, saying:

"That, my good man, is a half-ruble. Take two kopecks, for the love of Christ, and give me forty-eight in change."

The blind man took the half-ruble and slipped it in his pocket. He recommenced his litany: "Christians, good people, give alms to a poor blind man!"

"But what is happening, little father?" said the boy. "Give me my change, and do it at once!"

The blind man was stony, and said insolently and slyly:

"I thank you for your alms, my good man; go on your way."

"You are making fun of me! Give me my change, old rascal! I still have more than forty versts to travel today, and I shall need it badly en route."

The blind man pretended not to hear him and took up his chant more enthusiastically than ever. "Christians, good people, give alms to a poor blind man!"

Then the boy became enraged.

"See here, you scoundrel, give me my money, or I am going to settle the account in my own way!" he declared. He began to hit the old man and to shake him energetically, but the latter countered by yelling as loudly as he could: "Help, thief! Gentle Jesus, I am being robbed! Help! Help me!"

At that the young man let go of him. "It is better," he thought, "to flee the temptation to commit a sin. Besides, I risk having the police arrive and put me in prison for a half-ruble!" So he continued on his way. After taking about ten steps, he stopped and turned around toward the blind man. He bitterly regretted the loss of his last kopecks.

When the blind beggar thought that the young man had left, he decided he had enough and could return home. He groped around to find his crutches and said gaily to them: "What do you think about it, my dear crutches? Is it not time for us to go home?" And he went off in the direction of his house.

The boy, for his part, followed him at a distance. His eyes left him. After a moment he observed two cabins at the edge of the forest. The blind man loosened his belt, took a key from it, and opened the door of one of them. While he once more took his crutches and closed his belt, the boy quickly slipped into the cabin, sat down on a bench and held his breath. The blind man then entered his dwelling place, set the latch, threw off his back pack and his cap and crawled under the stove, causing a pot and a fire iron to clatter. He took a little barrel into which he threw the money. This being done, he said laughingly: "Thanks to the boy who today gave me the gift of a half-ruble, I now have five hundred." And overcome with joy simply at the thought, he seated himself on the ground, his legs spread wide, and rolled the little barrel in front of him as if playing with a toy. He sent it against the wall, then pulled it back.

Seeing this, our friend was seized by a fit of anger. "Wait a little, rogue, and I will spoil your pleasure!" He bent over and, from the bench, adroitly stopped the little barrel as it passed. "It must have been caught under the table," thought the blind man, and he began to search on the ground, but he could find nothing. At that point the man became anguished beyond description. He opened the door and called to his comrade, who was also blind:

"Brother, come quickly; come, for I have need of you!"

"What is the matter?" asked his neighbor, approaching.

The beggar told him the story of the little barrel full of money.

"You should always be careful about thieves!" his companion told him. "You had a notion to play with your wealth, and now you are sorry. Besides, what good is a small barrel? If only you had done as I did! I also have five hundred rubles, but I took the precaution of sewing them in my old cap. You cannot imagine anyone taking them from me."

As soon as he heard these words, the boy jumped from the bench and, as speedy as the wind, snatched the blind man's cap, went out of the door in a single leap and left running.

However, the neighbor blamed his companion in misery.

"No, my brother, all the same you cannot do that to me! It is not because you have lost your money that you can think that you can now take mine!"

They grabbed each other by the hair, each trying to throw down the other, and wrestled until they were exhausted.

And while they were struggling, the young man continued on his

195

way. He arrived home and rejoined his family, with whom he lived very happily. And long afterward, he was still telling his grandchildren how he had once gotten the best of two old knaves.

Martha and Mary

Once upon a time there were two sisters of noble blood, one of whom was named Martha and the other Mary.

Mary married a man who was named John and who lived in the country of Murom, while Martha wed a bourgeois by the name of Longinus who took her to the country of Ryazan. John was of noble origin. On the other hand, he possessed few worldly goods. Longinus, for his part, was of less aristocratic birth but dit not lack for money.

Once upon a time there was a party at the home of Martha's and Mary's parents, to which everyone was invited and that became an occasion for conflict between the two families. As a matter of fact, the two husbands started to argue as to who was going to occupy the place of honor at the table. John felt that he was entitled to it because of his nobility, and Longinus was equally convinced that the honor should be his, because of his wealth. At that point the situation began to deteriorate, and in a short while the two brothers-in-law broke off completely with one another. They even went so far as to forbid their wives to write each other or ever to see one another again to the day of their deaths.

Many years later, the men whom we are discussing, John and Longinus, gave up the ghost on the same day, at the same hour.

Their wives, Martha and Mary, being quite unaware of this coincidence, both felt grief in their hearts and sadness in their souls.

Mary thoughts, deep down inside: "I am going to the home of Longinus, my brother-in-law, to pay my sister a visit. I am welcome there, I shall live with them. If they reject my advances, at least I shall have had the opportunity to be reconciled with my sister."

Meanwhile Martha, for her part, decided to follow the dictates of her heart and her conscience. "I will go find John, my sister's husband. If they want to make me welcome, I will make them a gift of everything I have inherited. Thus they will be as wealthy as was my husband." And both of them left their respective homes on the same day. Their paths crossed, and they set up their tents only a short distance apart.

The younger sister sent a servant to gather information. His mission was to discover who had camped nearby. "If it is a woman," thought Mary, "why should we not meet? If it is a man, I have no desire to make his acquaintance." The servant went to find the facts from Martha's servants. He learned that the person camping nearby was a widow and that she was going to Murom to visit her sister.

He went black and informed his mistress about what he had been told. And that was how it happened that the two sisters came into each other's presence, greeted one another and embraced; however, they failed to recognize each other. But in the course of their conversation, they asked each other for their names and backgrounds and learned the truth. There followed an explosion of joy. And they hugged one another, laughing and crying at the same time. They were saddened by the loss of their respective spouses, even though the latter had not given them the love for which they had hoped, but their principal regret was that they had lost all contact because of the husbands and that they had neither seen nor written to one another for so many years on end. Yet what happiness they experienced at the thought that God had seen fit to reunite them at the end of their lives!

A meal was prepared, and they ate and drank to the glory of the Lord. They were merry. They retired, their hearts filled with joy, and went to sleep in the same tent, dozing fitfully.

It was at that point that an angel appeared to them. He gave them gold and silver, gold to Martha and silver to Mary, and ordered them to donate these riches to the first persons they might encounter the following day. In the dream, they took the gold and the silver and concealed it in their wide sleeves.

The two sisters woke up and told each other about their dream. Martha spoke first.

"There appeared before me an angel who said to me: 'The Lord sends you gold to reward you for your faith; make a cross out of it, and it will create life.' Furthermore, he advised me to give the gold to the first people I met."

She looked in her sleeve and found the gold there. Mary took up the account:

"The same thing happened to me, my sister. To me, too, an angel appeared. He gave me silver and counseled me to make from it a shrine for the cross that creates life."

She also looked in her sleeve and found the silver there. They began to weep for joy and to thank God in their prayers for the miracle that he had wrought.

Just then they saw three monks, who were coming in their direction. The women greeted them and recounted what they had seen in their dream.

"We know everything, and it is not by chance alone that we are here," the monks responded.

The women gave them the gold and silver and asked them to make a cross and a shrine as the angel had ordered. The brothers promised to obey the demand of God and retraced their steps.

Martha and Mary, for their part, continued on their way until they reached Murom. They related to their families all that had happened. Their auditors started to grumble. They did not appreciate the fact that the two sisters had handed over such a valuable treasure to some unknown monks.

"Was there not then any goldsmith or silversmith in our town who would have been capable of fashioning a cross from the gold and a shrine from the silver?" they asked.

"But we acted according to divine instructions," answered the two sisters, amazed at the lack of confidence.

The news spread like wildfire. Everyone around deplored the loss of the gold and silver. They decided to look for the fathers and the treasure they were holding. Each nobleman was accompanied by a servant who did not belong to him, and each servant by a master he was not accustomed to serve, these precautions being taken to insure that no one would succumb to the temptation to steal the precious metals.

Parting by different paths, they soon rejoined one another, and it was not long afterward that they recognized the three monks. They were walking single file, carrying a cross of pure gold and a shrine of shining silver. The young servants were prepared to seize them, but the brothers forestalled them.

"Do not act rashly, for you will regret it," they said.

At these words, the noblemen and their vassals forbade the horsemen to touch the servants of God. They got down from their horses and knelt as the monks passed.

The brothers, for their part, continued on their way until they reached the two sisters. They said to Martha and Mary:

"An angel of the Lord appeared to you and gave you gold and silver, that you handed over to us so that we could manufacture this silver shrine. By respecting the Divine Word, you have participated in the salvation of the world."

Martha and Mary questioned the monks, wanting to know where they came from.

"From Constantinople, that is also called Zarenbourg."

They also asked how much time it had taken them to cover the distance that separated them from that city.

"Almost three hours," they said simply.

"Do you wish to eat or drink?"

"We have no appetite."

They withdrew and were never seen again.

Martha and Mary placed the silver shrine and the gold cross in the church of the archangel Michael, where they are still to be found today, creating life and curing any illness.

Legend of the Russian priest

In the heart of Russia, in a desert by the name of Kamenka, rose a church dedicated to the Virgin. When the Poles, who knew nothing about God, destroyed Moscow, they also invaded this desert, where there lived only one solitary monk.

One of the Poles then entered the church, dragging a captive behind him. The father, panic-stricken, took refuge in the main altar, where he hid. And from there he observed the Pole. He saw him approach, and even dare lay his hands on an image of the Virgin, which he carried to the far end of the church. He threw it to the ground and copulated with the captive woman on top of the holy figure.

The monk, who had watched to his horror every detail of the scene, wept hot tears. He addressed the mother of God: "Oh, Holy Virgin, You who gave birth to Christ our Lord, why do you let this accursed pagan sully Your church; how can you accept the fact that his infamous act has soiled your portrait? Why do You not reduce him to nothingness?"

It was then that a voice answered him: "Oh, servant of God, let me assure you that this madman will be punished. Do not concern yourself about him; his end will not be an enviable one. But let Me also add this: this heretic has behaved less badly toward Me than you yourself. For it is without fear that you enter My church in the morning, and without hesitation that you approach the chalice. Now, what did you do the previous evening? You drank more than you should have, you were intoxicated beyond the bounds of reason, and the next day, you breathed on My image with a breath stinking of alcohol. Has it never occurred to you that these repugnant exhalations sully My image even more than the sacrilege committed by a man who does not know God? He will be punished, certainly, but he acted without realizing what he was doing. You, on the other hand, are perfectly familiar with all the sins. Verily, I say unto you, before it is too late repent and renounce the life you are leading."

And the voice became silent.

The Pole, finally having an intimation of the power of God, fled from the church and disappeared, while the father arose, transformed, and lived out his life austerely.

Printed by
Officine Grafiche
de Aldo Garzanti Editore s.p.a.
Milano

Printed in Italy